WHAT HAPPENED
TO THE GAME I LOVED?

First Published in Great Britain in 2018 by DB Publishing,
an imprint of JMD Media Ltd

ISBN 9781780915821

Printed and bound in the UK

WHAT HAPPENED
TO THE GAME I LOVED?

ANDY MURDOCK

Chapter 1

Wee Dave

Shorts, shirt, left sock, right sock, left boot, right boot and finally slip the shin pads in. Wee Dave was in the middle of his usual pre-match routine, but full of nerves and anxious that the rest of the team could hear the banging of his heart.

A small creature has definitely climbed under my skin, got stuck in my ribcage and is trying to break free, he thought to himself.

Wee Dave, as his name suggests, is a very little fella, normal by looks and normal by nature. He has short dark hair which is swept to the side at the front, a button nose and a cheeky little smile showing dimples on both cheeks.

This smile was not evident as he stared around the changing room, mirroring the blank faces of his teammates as they listened to the drone of Coach Alan's voice.

I wonder if this is something important, he thought. Nobody else seemed interested, but then again, they'd been here so many times.

'Right boys, first game of the season. Let's continue from last year and no mistakes! Get out there and win!' A solitary clap thundered from Coach Alan's shovels before he went to each player in turn to give them some individual advice.

Last season, The Buccaneer Falls won an incredible double, the first in their history, guided by the most sought-after manager in the game, Coach Alan. But Wee Dave was the new signing... 'A guaranteed success,' said his agent; 'A future star,' said the experts. But also a big risk to the successful squad of last season, and Coach Alan was not a man who took risks.

Wee Dave saw the beads of sweat running down Coach Alan's forehead as he approached, having to stoop low to avoid banging his head on the ceiling, but still towering over Wee Dave, who was by now huddled in the corner, trying to hide from the gigantic belly that faced him.

All had gone dark – a puff of Wee Dave's cheeks, an inward breath, oh my, the whiff of stale sweat almost making him puke.

'Do what you do best,' Coach Alan grumbled, 'I want to see goals.'

'Yes Coach,' Wee Dave squeaked.

After a pat on the back – more like a sledgehammer – Coach Alan squeezed through the door without another word and the team were on their feet, raring to go.

'Let's go lads!'

'We've got this!'

'From the start!'

Wee Dave joined the tail end as the Buccaneer Falls walked

through the famous corridor towards the field. Moving his head from side to side he looked at every player on the Wall of Fame and imagined each one giving him advice as he passed, especially the final player, his favourite player: Stan.

Closing his eyes and taking a deep breath, Wee Dave wondered if Stan had ever felt like this.

Nobody has ever felt like this!

The team came to a halt at the legendary first step, the '*Good Old Buccaneers*' painted across it in brown and red letters.

Wee Dave's heart was somersaulting, butterflies flying, face as white as a ghost, sweat dripping from every pore and knees knocking like the clappers. Looking through the hips and legs in front of him and focussing his eyes on that first step, he made himself a promise not to look up until he reached the step. Was this the first step towards stardom? Or would he fall at the first step?

Wee Dave had been a Buccaneers fan since he was twelve years old, attending matches with his best mate and old coach on a regular occasion, so in his head he sang along with the supporters as they launched into their traditional rendition of 'The Good Old Buccaneers', which was sung at the start of every game.

As the noise faded away, more cries of 'Come on lads!' were heard amid the cracking of studs as the team moved forward and onto the field.

At the first step Wee Dave looked up through his new teammates, seeing the clear blue skies and the football-shaped clouds, clouds which had followed him from the beginning.

What a beautiful day for my debut, he thought, taking a deep breath. *The fans, the weather… this is what I've been working my entire life for, this is my dream, pull yourself together!*

Another deep breath.

Second step. He had not fallen over!

I've done it, I'm here.

Third step. Was that a cheeky little smile forming? Two dimples becoming bigger as thoughts of his childhood and playing with his mates were coming to fruition.

Fourth step. 'Relaaaax.' The voice of his wise old coach, who he knew would be watching from the stands.

Five.

Six.

Seven.

Eight.

By the time Wee Dave had arrived at the twelfth and final step, his nerves had been replaced by excitement, the wall of brown and red from the supporters coming into view to go with the incredible NOISE they were creating. What a sensation for Wee Dave to be on the receiving end of what can only be described as a thunderstorm of an atmosphere.

As he took it all, in he thought, *I've done it, this is the start of something special, I have the world at my feet and I am going to make the most of it.*

This was Wee Dave's professional debut, he was fourteen years old.

Chapter 2

Building Blocks

Wee Dave has had a ball at his feet for as long he can remember.

'I swear you were born with a ball stuck to that left foot, boy,' his Uncle Billy always said.

His first memory of football was when Dad and his friends were at the house to watch a big game. He'd stared in wonder at the costumes the group were wearing and found it strange yet intriguing as they pointed and yelled at the TV.

He fought with all his might to stay awake and watch his dad – he adored his dad, everyone loves their dad… but his eyes were heavy and each time his head lolled to the side he would jerk himself awake and try again. But his heavy head got the better of him and he lay it on his favourite black and white pillow. A pillow he hugged as if his life depended on it, his best friend who he would never let go. Doze, dozzzeee, dooozzzzeeeeee…

'YAAAAASSSSS!!!' roared the group of men, startling Wee Dave into an upright position, as golden milk sprayed all over him, the sour smell and taste making Wee Dave feel faint. He watched on in amazement as the group formed a circle and were jumping up and down, still shouting at the tops of their lungs.

Wee Dave looked up to his dad, thought he was the coolest thing on the planet – except for his pillow, of course – and wanted to be just like him. So the next morning, he took it upon himself to copy his dad while watching his favourite cartoons.

'WHAT IS ALL THIS RACKET?' Mum screamed, entering the living room, sleeves rolled up and ready for the bell. She looked at the mess on the floor, shook her head, raised her eyebrows and with her hands on her hips she said, 'Oh David, what am I going to do with you?'

The next week, when Dad's friends returned, he made sure to study their cartoon in more detail. Maybe this would help to explain why the men were allowed to act like they did.

The first sign of confusion for Wee Dave was that the cartoons were not bright and shiny, they were real people, and they wore the same outfit as Dad. Standing shoulder to shoulder with their hands on their chest they were belting out some song.

Hey! That looks like my pillow, Wee Dave thought as he looked from the TV to his pillow and back to the TV again. A moment later, the man holding the pillow put it on the ground and after a high-pitched whistle the men on the TV were kicking it. Wee Dave was horrified.

You are supposed to put that under your head!

This time, Dad and his mates were not so happy, rather than cheering they were jeering, rather than smiles there were snarls. But Wee Dave took no notice, the game on TV had mesmerised him and he wanted to try it.

So he grabbed his pillow and set it carefully on the floor, took two steps back and with a swing of his left foot the pillow was in the air. Wee Dave's jaw dropped as he gaped after the ball which was sailing straight towards his dad's nose. Time stood still. Dad ducked and tried to put his hands in the way, but too late, the ball clattered off the top of his head! Not only that, but while trying to block it, one of his hands knocked over his bottle of golden milk and glass shattered everywhere. Dad's face went bright red.

'Yeeeeoooooooo!!' his friends cried through fits of laughter, before yelling, 'No more drink for you, no more drink for you, no more drink, no more drink, no more drink for you!'

'That's some left peg young Dave has!' one said, still trying to catch his breath.

Dad laughed it off after clearing up the mess and Wee Dave felt proud, he must have done something good because the mood in the room went from mad to merry as the adults discussed that 'wand of a left foot'.

Wands are magic, thought Wee Dave, *I must be a wizard.*

From that night, Wee Dave took his ball everywhere, from his bedroom to the bathroom, from the living room to the kitchen. He even brought it shopping with Mum.

Dad was delighted, but Mum was peeved.

'David is kicking that ball everywhere,' she said after dinner.

'Well that's brilliant, isn't it? He's going to be an outstanding little player, I know it!' Dad replied. 'You shoulda heard the lads talking about that left peg of his!'

'That's all well and good,' came back Mum, 'but this house is no place for him to be kicking a football. On Monday he hit me in the back of the head and I was close to dropping a glass of juice.

And yesterday, he kicked it to the top of the stairs while I was coming down with the laundry.'

'Oh wow!! Was it from his hands or the floor?'

'It's not funny, sweetheart, I could have fallen down and injured myself. If it happens again, that ball is gone.'

'I suppose you're right,' Dad conceded. 'I'll take him to the Park at the weekend.'

The shot that Mum was talking about was not from Wee Dave's hands. He had invented a game called the Ladder. Starting from the first step, he tried to hit them all in order and if he messed up, he would start again from the bottom.

Looking up it seemed impossible to begin with, like the bottom of Mount Everest, but the more he practised the higher up the Ladder he got. It soon became easy to hit the first seven steps in a row but he kept messing up at the eighth.

He tried and tried and tried for over an hour until he finally got to step nine, and as the ball came back down Wee Dave got nervous, took a big swish and completely missed it. Falling to the floor, he looked at the ceiling in despair.

I'm never going to get this, he thought, elbow throbbing from the pain of the fall. *Even if I do get to step ten, there are still three after that.* Wee Dave closed his eyes and took a deep breath.

Come on, you're special, you have a magic left foot!

He got up from the floor, dusted himself off, and having given himself a pep talk about how he was going to succeed, he failed at the third step. Another hour passed in which he got to step ten a few times but failed because of his overexcitement.

Last go.

Last go.

Last go, Wee Dave kept thinking, but it never was.

Finally, he got to the eleventh.

Yes, I've done it! But not finished yet. Two more to go.

The ball came bounding down towards him and with all of his focus, he swung his left leg at the ball.

Twelve, done easily.

Last one. Keep that focus. Eyes on the ball. Kick.

He caught it clean and as the ball left his foot he knew he had completed the Ladder. Just as he was wheeling away in celebration, Mum came to the top step and volleyed the ball straight back down the stairs.

'Right, that's it,' she shrieked, 'that ball is going away for the rest of the day.'

The seat belt annoyed Wee Dave, making him feel trapped, confined to the back of Dad's car.

Are we there yet? Are we there yet? Are we there yet?

Straining his neck he tried with all of his might to see out the window, but he was too small, only big enough to look up into the blue skies, blue skies with football clouds. Hugging his football close to his chest he noticed that everything in the car was a football, the gearstick, the steering wheel, the mirrors, even the back of Dad's head!

Dad and Wee Dave were on their way to the Park to play football. It had not been a good week! Mum had banned his ball after he smashed an old family lamp into smithereens, and not knowing what else to do, he started kicking everything within distance of his left foot.

'GET HIM TO THE PARK!' Mum screamed.

'You're right, we'll go on Sunday.' Turning to Wee Dave, Dad said that he'd better behave or he would not go.

'It's a huge space son, and you can kick the ball as far as you like without anyone shouting at you.'

Wee Dave could not stop thinking about the Park after this, and although Mum had banned his football, she could not stop his dreams. The night of the argument he completed the Ladder while celebrating with Dad over lots of spilled milk. Even Mum joined in!

Dad rolled the window down on entering the Park and Wee Dave stretched his neck as far as he could, but all he could see was a spotty teenager in a little house, each spot transformed into a football.

'How much for an hour?' Dad asked.

'How old?' mumbled Spotman.

'Four and a half.'

'That will be 500 credits,' Spotman said, holding out a card with a barcode, while Dad took his phone from his pocket. After pushing the screen a few times and holding his phone to the card, there was a beep of approval and Spotman handed Dad a slip of paper.

'Four- and five-year-olds are on the first floor. We're not very busy today so choose whichever door is available,' Spotman said and put some fluffy headphones over his ears. Fluffy headphones that were shaped liked footballs.

Dad drove on and the blue skies and football clouds were replaced by a grey ceiling which seemed miles away, even further than the sky. When the car came to a stop Dad unbuckled Wee Dave, and like a dog being let off its leash he jumped out of the car, ready for whatever was in front of him. But he soon realised that he didn't know what to do, didn't know where to go, so he turned impatiently to Dad, waving at him to hurry up.

The Park was a huge mass of grey... grey walls, grey ceiling, and as Wee Dave trotted across the grey floor, his feet felt heavy.

'Impressive, isn't it?' Dad said, putting his hands to his hips and looking around. 'A hundred storeys high, over a thousand football pitches here, son.'

The two of them stood at the bottom floor, staring in amazement. It was the biggest place that Wee Dave had ever been, walkways vanishing into the distance lining the sides of each floor. Wee Dave's heart skipped with excitement when he looked through the rusty iron bars and saw the bright green football pitches, somehow looking even greener in the grey surroundings. The echo of a football could be heard in the distance.

'First floor, son, we can use the stairs,' Dad pointed and Wee Dave followed, each step groaning with displeasure and coughing up dust as they climbed.

Man in Black. Man in Black. Man in Black.

On the outside of every pitch was a Man in Black. Black boots, black trousers, black shirt, and arms the size of legs folded across barrel chests. Wee Dave's eyes moved to the head and face...

Mouth... nothing else. Wee Dave gripped his Dad's trousers, pointing at the face of each Man in Black who had no eyes, no nose, no eyebrows. Only a mouth.

'Don't worry, son, they're the MouthMen, they're here to protect us,' Dad reassured him.

A man and a boy of around the same age as Wee Dave appeared at one of the fields. *Wow*, Wee Dave thought as he watched the boy glide with the ball, avoiding a lot of red and white spots on the ground. In all of Wee Dave's excitement of kicking the ball as far as he could, he had never thought of keeping the ball close to his feet.

'We'll take the next one,' Dad whispered.

'Ticket,' the Mouth said.

Dad held out the receipt for the MouthMan to scan, and after a successful beep and a clunk of the lock, the MouthMan swung the door open with an almighty force.

'Sixty minutes,' MouthMan boomed after slamming the door behind them.

Wee Dave didn't know where to start or what to do, so he decided to hug his football tight to his chest and hide behind Dad's leg.

'Go on, son, use that left foot of yours, let's see what your Mum has been fussing over.'

Wee Dave's bottom lip started to quiver, he didn't know what to do! Looking across to see what the other boy was doing his vision was blocked by the wall between the fields, but he could hear the lightness of the boy's steps and the echo of the ball.

Dad crouched down to eye level. 'Come on, son, it's okay, let's pretend we're in the house and there's no one else here.' He held his hands out and asked for the football. Reluctant, Wee Dave turned away. 'Okay, we can go home then?' Dad said, starting to walk for the door. Wee Dave froze to the spot, not following Dad this time. 'Oh David, make up your mind, do we stay or do we go?'

Wee Dave let go of the ball, swinging his left leg at it, and seconds later it was sailing through the air. He looked to Dad who sprinted towards him, beaming, hands held out.

'Brilliant, son, gimme five!'

Wee Dave sprinted to retrieve the ball and tried again. Swing, kick, ball in the air, high fives, sprint, swing, kick, ball in the air, high fives…

Remembering the gliding boy beside him, Wee Dave decided to try to run with the ball close to his feet. However, he stumbled, tripped and fell flat on his face, scraping his hands on the ground in the process. He looked at Dad, who was smiling encouragement at him.

'No worries, son, keep trying…'

He tried and fell. He tried and fell. He tried and fell. He tried and fell. He tried and fell. He tried…

BUUUUUZZZZZZZZ!!!!!

A thunderous alarm filled the air which was followed by the MouthMan heaving the door open. What felt like five minutes was actually an hour.

'Time's up.' The mouth had spoken.

Wee Dave looked at Dad, pleading with his eyes.

'Let's go, son,' Dad said. 'We'll come back again next week, and the week after that, and the week after.'

Wee Dave dropped his head, and scooping the ball under his left arm, he trudged through the door without another word. The echo of the ball from the next field and the tip-tap of the footsteps could still be heard and Wee Dave stopped to gaze through the bars.

He is so lucky, he thought. *I wonder how long he has been in there…*

The boy, kitted in red shirt, white shorts and red socks, was still gliding like a swan, ball seemingly stuck to his foot. After getting through the discs on the ground he unleashed a strike with his right foot which made an almighty thud off the padded wall and came back to his feet. Wee Dave watched in despair.

There's no way I'll ever be that good!

Wee Dave then looked at the boy's father, his fat father who wore an all-white suit and shiny pointed shoes. His fat father with a skinny face, chin like an arrow whose beak was buried in his phone. His fat father who, like his son, had his dark hair slicked back and glued to his head. His fat father who did not even acknowledge Wee Dave and Dad looking in.

'Good afternoon, Mr Slyme,' Dad said to the man.

Clearly annoyed and not wishing to speak, Mr Slyme replied, 'Good afternoon, Sir.'

'Boy's looking good. Been here long?'

'About three hours now. One more hour and he'll be done.'

'Well... enjoy the rest of your weekend, see you tomorrow.' Dad waved and smiled at him but there was no response.

Trapped under his seat belt again, the grey ceilings of the Park were replaced by the blue skies and football clouds as Dad explained that he worked with Mr Slyme at the Bank, that he was the owner of the Park and that he was a good man to know.

Wee Dave had forgotten about the Slymes, he had forgotten about football. In the car ride home he just wanted Dad to stop blabbering. Although he'd had an amazing time at the Park, all he wanted at this very moment in time was to scoff ice cream and watch cartoons.

'Please, Dad,' Wee Dave pleads. 'Pleeeeeaaaaaasssse! I want more!'

They are on the way home in the car after another Sunday at the Park, this argument becoming a ritual for Wee Dave. This was the worst time of his week, because he knew it was the longest time before he could play football again. It made him angry. It made him sad. And when Wee Dave is angry and sad, Wee Dave is annoying.

'Son, we do not have enough money.'

'What about Slyme?'

'I've told you a million times, David, they own the Park, they can play when they like.'

'Why don't you own the Park?' Wee Dave huffed and folded his arms, frowning his eyebrows and scrunching his nose so tight that it hurt his face.

This was usually when Dad lost his temper, but this time he took a deep breath and didn't answer. Wee Dave didn't know what to do, so he just sat in silence.

I can play the silent game longer than him, he thought, moving his head around, looking everywhere but at Dad. A few moments later he let out a breath, then another, and another, getting louder each time, but he could not get Dad's attention. He slid down the car seat as far as he could, lifted one knee to his face and in a cycling motion was kicking the back of the driver's seat.

'David... David... David!!'

Aha, I have his attention now.

'One more time and we'll not go back to the Park!'

Wee Dave sucked the air in, held his breath and sat like a statue. *No Park? I can't live with no Park! What do I do now?* He gripped the ball tighter to his chest, rested his cheek on it and tried to fall asleep. But he couldn't, the thoughts of Slyme being at the Park every day haunted him. *It's so unfair, he gets to play when he wants and I only play once a week. I wish I was Slyme, I wish Slyme's dad was my dad.*

He had been going to the Park every Sunday for almost a year now and had improved every week, especially since his dad had started playing one-on-one against him.

'I'll be in this goal, you be in that goal,' Dad said, pointing to the goal for Wee Dave to go in. 'I'll be The Buccaneers and you can be City, the best team in all of the land!'

Dad came charging like a bull towards him, stole it from his feet and scored. Wee Dave watched him wheel away in celebration, yelling 1–0. 'Your turn, you must be quicker next time.'

Same again, Dad came thundering but Wee Dave was quicker this time, nudging the ball to the side and running away and… BANG, straight into the wall. The top of his head was throbbing with pain, he put his hand to it but this didn't help. Checking his hand for any sign of blood… none there. He looked to his dad for sympathy, wanting to bawl and cry his eyes out, but was met with the sound of his dad's laughter.

'1–0. Next time, look where you're going.'

Wee Dave forgot about the pain, and clenching his fists together, he took the ball, dribbled forward, touched it to the side of Dad, looked to see which direction he was going and… 1–1. He had scored! His heart thundered inside him. He had just scored a goal. His dad lifted him in the air and Wee Dave was on top of the world. He had scored! He had scored a goal! Wow!!

'Nooooo!' Dad moaned after Wee Dave had scored the winner to make it 10–9. He raised his arms, jumping up and down, pointing at Dad, grabbing the ball, kicking it in the air, doing anything he could to keep moving. When he stopped celebrating and stood still for a second he could feel the cold patch of sweat on the back of his shirt.

They played like this every week, with Wee Dave thinking he was getting better, but unable to understand why he kept winning 10–9. *Why can I not win 10–8? I need to get better for next week!*

One week, Dad looked over to Mr Slyme.

'Fancy a challenge?' he called. 'My lad versus your lad?'

Mr Slyme looked Wee Dave up and down and with a smirk replied, 'Sure.'

Wee Dave had won every game he had ever played… and against an adult. There was no way a little kid was going to beat him!

The dads stepped to the side, dropped a ball in the middle and the sons were in play. Like a flash of lightning, Slyme was on the ball, attacking Wee Dave, and as soon as he got close he drifted to the side and was gone before Wee Dave could even blink. 1–0.

It soon became 2–0, then 5–0 and Wee Dave got more and more dejected, looking for his Dad as the game passed him by. After being humiliated 10–0 in the space of three minutes he walked over to Dad, and with his head flopping to the ground he quivered, 'I'm not playing anymore. Never again!'

At the other side of the field, the Slymes' heads were hung back, howling with laughter. Wee Dave saw this and although he tried really hard, he could not hold back the tears. He had let his dad down. He had let himself down. To add to this, Dad was going to shout at him for this disgraceful defeat.

Wee Dave was surprised when Dad was smiling. 'Don't worry kid, you were great.'

Maybe he hadn't let his family down, but at the end of the day his football career was over, so with a drop of the head he gathered his bag and whimpered, 'Let's go, Dad.'

In the car Dad tried to console Wee Dave but he was having none of it, he just stared out of the window at the clear blue skies, which had no football clouds today. Dad slowed the car, but they weren't home, Wee Dave could still see the high buildings of 10/10, and when the car stopped Wee Dave saw the huge letters spelling out FOOD.

Dad was out of the car and around to Wee Dave's door in no time. On his honkers and grabbing him by both shoulders he said,

'Listen, son. There are two ways to go about this. One: you can feel sorry for yourself. Or two: you can use today as a lesson and make yourself better. It's up to you to decide. Come on, you'll love this.'

With that, Dad took Wee Dave's hand, brought him into the chippy and bought a Cowboy Supper. As the smell of salt and vinegar chips hit his nose, Wee Dave thought about what Dad had just said to him. He was right of course, Wee Dave did not want to be humiliated like that again… So was this the time to give up? Or would this be used as part of a learning curve to make him better?

As we already know, Wee Dave did not give up, he chose the latter. He remembered these wise words from Dad for the rest of his life, and anytime that things were bleak, he knew that to get better, he would have to try harder.

How could he have ever thought of giving up the beautiful game of football? Before he had even started! Wee Dave's mind wandered to the taste of the sausage, beans and chips, all thoughts of the morning's game erased.

Chapter 3

School

David Blanch
Number 36
Street -65
Road 31

Dear David,
We are pleased to inform you that, due to your outstanding score on the entrance exam, you have been added to the list of potential football players for the future, and therefore have been accepted to the School. Please find attached a list of ebooks for you to study before the start of term. You will also need to complete the necessary forms and send them to us to acknowledge your acceptance.

Sincerely,
Mr Stout (MBE, OBE, RBE, MSc, Dr, Jr, TSL, Jnr, Br)
Head of Sport
Chief Executive League of the Sky

```
Professor in Football
Head Scout
League of the Sky Legend
Vice Chairman
Vice Chancellor
Vice President
Chief Minister
```

Wee Dave had grown enough that he could see the road signs as Mum drove him to School for his first day. Having been taught how to read by the family iPad – Mum explained the importance of this – Wee Dave used the road signs as practice.

Street – 65, Street – 64, Street – 63, Street – 62... When they reached Street –10, the tick-tock of the indicators was heard before Mum turned the car to the right... Road 31, Road 30, Road 29, Road 28... At Road 10 they had to go through a toll to enter 10/10, the centre of Middleton where everything could be found.

Wee Dave stared at the huge red letters on the side of each building and practised his reading some more.

PARK, MOVIES, MUSIC, FOOD, CLOTHES, BANK.

The words ran up the sides of their respective buildings, from the ground to the heavens. So much so that Wee Dave's eyes were stinging with pain, the letters too far away, so deciding to rest them, he closed his eyes. In doing so he could feel the drumming of his heart, in fact the beating seemed to be everywhere. In his ears, in his arms, in his legs, even his fingers...

What if no one likes me? These kids are going to be much smarter than me. I don't wanna go!

When he reopened his eyes he was faced with... SCHOOL.

'Okay David, here we are. Now remember, follow the signs for SPORT and then FOOTBALL. Couldn't be easier.'

She kissed his forehead and told him that everything would be okay. He stared after the car until it had disappeared, then stared a little longer, hoping it would return, but it didn't.

He was alone.

The buzzing in the air, the heat, the sweat, the stench, the hustle of thousands of other kids, young and old, backpack, backpack, backpack. Laughter. Crying. Crying children. Crying mums. Screeching mums. Bright red faces, mouths agape, sniffling noses. Oh... one boy had just tripped on his laces and his lunch had gone everywhere. Older kids pointed and laughed.

Wee Dave spotted a gap and joined the march of the penguins outside the School, reading the signs above each door he passed. LAW, MUSIC, ENGINEERING, IT, NUTRITION. After seeing SPORT he veered to the left, taking many backpack shots to the head and even more kicks to the ankle, and joined a line of students, each being checked by MouthMen.

Beep, approved.

Beep, approved.

BUZZZZZZZ!

'Social Science is three doors that way,' MouthMan said to the rejected student in front of Wee Dave. 'NEXT!' Wee Dave held out his passport and acceptance letter.

Beep, approved.

'First year, five years old, Football, third elevator to the right, bottom floor. NEXT!'

Wee Dave shuffled his way to the third elevator on the right and on entering, he had to suck in his breath along with everyone else, just so they could squeeze in. As the cage dropped 100 floors

Wee Dave's stomach tried to jump out of his mouth, and he really had to battle with himself to hold in the vomit. Unfortunately, this was not the case for three other boys who threw up everywhere, the bile floating in the air and sticking to the roof of the elevator. The smell was putrid.

When the doors opened everyone bundled out, falling on top of each other. Wee Dave brushed himself off, glad to get out of the sickly smell of the cart, and looked down at the giant screen.

WELCOME TO 1ST YEAR FOOTBALL

The block of seats to the right was full, and after being shepherded to the left he took his seat, No. 29, and began bouncing his knees in anticipation.

Waiting… his face flushed, his eyes darted in all directions, he did not know where to look or what to do. He saw one kid falling down the steps, causing a domino effect for the line in front.

Waiting… his face was hot, how he wished to be at home, in the comfort and cosiness of his bed.

Waiting… his face was burning, what was taking so long? His shins ached with the pain of his bouncing knees. He could taste the salt as the sweat poured onto his lips.

Waiting… his face was on fire!

Ten minutes had passed and Wee Dave's anxiety had reached new levels, when the screen began to flash.

'YOU WANT TO BE A FOOTBALL PLAYER!' bellowed a deep voice which echoed around the room. 'YOU WANT TO PLAY IN THE LEAGUE OF THE SKY!'

Wee Dave's heart drummed faster, did the voice have to be so LOUD!? He looked around and the majority of the class were nodding in agreement, others had slid down their chairs trying to hide, some were crying or holding their hands over their ears.

The screen had been blank for some time, until five footballers appeared on it, famous footballers, footballers from the League of the Sky, City players.

'LIVE IN UPPERTON!' boomed the voice. 'LOVE UPPERTON!'

Each player was recorded on the screen driving sports cars into huge driveways, swimming in their own pools, playing golf in the back garden, all waving happily at the camera. It then cut to them scoring goals for City, lifting trophies for City, celebrating in the red-and-white colours of City. Then there was footage of them playing when they were younger, when they were kids. At the end, the screen froze on an old photo of hundreds of boys sitting in a classroom, the very classroom that Wee Dave was sitting in. Five red circles appeared on the screen, highlighting the five kids who had evidently grown up to become a success.

The recording finished, the screen went blank, the lights came on and the class looked around in silence. A door opened at the bottom corner of the room, and a plump man in a black suit, white shirt and black tie waddled across the stage in front of the screen, followed by the five famous players who were wearing red-and-white tracksuits.

The plump man stood at a lectern and the players each took a seat to his side.

'Welcome to your first day of School, my name is Mr Stout.' He paused, amidst the sound of clapping from one student at the front, who stopped after realising he was alone, and there followed a stony silence. With a smile, Mr Stout continued.

'You have completed the questionnaires and have been sorted into separate classes to suit the needs of every student. At five and six years old, you are no longer children, you are old enough to make your own decisions and life choices.' He paused and snorted a little, looking to the players who were like statues in their seats.

'I am very glad that you have chosen to pursue a career in football, however, if you want to be good enough to play in the League of the Sky, it is essential that you show commitment and dedication from the start. That means from today!'

As he said 'today' he pointed his stubby finger on the lectern and he continued doing this with every word, like a dippy bird.

'That means from this very moment for the rest of your lives. We promise that if you do, we will guarantee that you have the greatest chance to go on and have a successful career in football.'

Like a god he opened his arms, rotating his body from side to side as he blabbed on.

'We will do everything within our powers to make sure you get there. Just look at these five chaps, they have worked hard, they are successful, they have lots of money and as we have seen… they are living happily in Upperton.'

Wee Dave had lost focus at the sound of Mr Stout's boring voice, and instead decided to dream in the direction of the players. One of them was called to the stage, which brought Wee Dave back to the moment.

'It seems like only a few years ago I was sitting where you are today. I'm sure you are very nervous, just like the five of us were,' he said in a dry tone, holding his palm in the direction of the other players. 'Mr Stout taught us everything we know, he took good care of us, guided us. The faith he and the School have put into me…'

Yadayadayada…Wee Dave's mouth opened in a yawn as his eyes began to droop. Half closed, fully closed, head drop, snoooozze… jerking his head up, eyes open… fully ALERT, looking everywhere, remembering where he was…

I need to stay awake, he thought. *Focus…*

'…you must work hard to get where we are.' Booorrrrrrring… Head drops again, to the side this time, ahhh, that's nice, eyes fully closed, the cool feel of his eyelids.

Wee Dave was awoken by the boy next door, who shrugged him off his shoulder in order to join in the applause.

'Great speech!' roared Mr Stout, clapping his hands more vigorously than anyone else in the room, looking like a seal who had just been rewarded. The clapping continued for another five minutes without a break, and just as it was fading Mr Stout cried, 'FANTASTIC!' and started to cheer at the top of his lungs. Around him, everyone got to their feet, so like a good little sheep Wee Dave rose with them.

There were another three rounds of this, which lasted thirty minutes, and eventually the five players were allowed to leave. Once everyone had settled down, Mr Stout began again.

'If you look at your desk you will see a key, turn this to the left, slide the drawer open and take out your iPad.' Clicking and sliding was heard as the class did as they were told.

'Each iPad and desk has the same number, you must log in with your details and this will be your number for the rest of the term.

Once you have logged in, there are simple step-by-step guides in order to obtain your timetable and start your lessons.'

Heads were buried into screens and silence ensued for the next two hours, except for the occasional cough or hiccup, until a whistle blasted in the air, piercing Wee Dave's ears and giving him a headache.

'Just like real football, each lesson will end with a final whistle. Once this blows, please pack your iPads into your desks and you can go home. See you tomorrow.'

Slide. Slam. Click. First day over.

They were shoulder to shoulder, full speed ahead, red-faced, spit snarling, breathing heavy, both sliding to the floor reaching their big toe as far as they could, stretch, stretch, stretch. *I must win this one*, the two of them thought. Both players got off the ground growling at each other. Still chasing, chasing and… GOAL!!

Wee Dave punched the ground in a rage before wiping the sweat off his face, running his hands through the little black stones which had nestled in his hair. His clothes were full of the black stones, they were everywhere, all over his body, scratches on his leg, itching like crazy. Oh, the stinging pain.

Get away from me, itch! Why was the itch always worse when he lost? He never felt the itch when he won.

When did that last happen? he thought. *Sure I always lose!*

Wee Dave looked to Slyme, who was lying on the ground with no energy left to celebrate, but finding something from somewhere to start laughing. Wee Dave stormed out of the Park without a word. *I'll never beat him!* he thought, after what must have been his millionth defeat.

On the way back to class Wee Dave was still fuming, thrusting his pass to the MouthMan, hitting the button in the elevator with extra vigour, hurling his bag before he even got to his seat and when he got there, he slid so far down that the back of his neck rested on the wooden bench.

Every day was the same for Wee Dave in those first three years at School. These were meant to be the Glory Years, the years of play, the years when teachers left them to experiment with their iPads, with the football, to do their own thing and have fun. After all, once they became eight years old, the serious work would to begin.

Glory Years, my arse, thought Wee Dave as he stared at the ceiling.

But with all of the negative thoughts, Wee Dave would come back the next day with new-found optimism, excited that this was going to be the day that he finally beat Slyme, but it always ended in defeat, always ended with him huffing for the rest of the day and night.

For the first year, Wee Dave tried to play with the School iPad, but sliding his finger across the screen… it was so boring, it hurt his eyes. So although he hated getting beaten by Slyme, being trapped in the confines of the Park was the only time he felt free. The only time he lived in the moment. And after all, this was going to be the day he finally won against…

Why the hell has Stout given me this team!? he thought, looking around at his three teammates. Fooley, a notorious stone eater and nose picker; Dozey, who took a nap at the side of the pitch; and Smiler, who just ran around with a smile on his face. *Six- and seven-year-olds doing this, what chance do I have?*

Well… Wee Dave battled his heart out that day, chasing every ball, defending, attacking, goalkeeping, he was everywhere, making up for his disastrous teammates. He scored some brilliant goals with his left foot, at times he dribbled through the entire opposition. He made many last-ditch tackles to save goals. He covered every blade of grass, but it was not enough to win. In fact, it was not enough to get beat.

His had been humiliated, 28–4.

Glory Years, my arse!

The next day, Stout had given them the exact same teams but switched Wee Dave and Slyme.

I'm not taking this lightly, thought Wee Dave, glaring at Slyme who returned his customary snarl. After the final whistle had blown, and Wee Dave's team had demolished Slyme and co. 15–1, Wee Dave thought back to the first time they had played each other, to the years of humiliation at the hands of Slyme.

I'm not letting this rest!

However, when he looked at Slyme, he was sitting on the ground, head buried between his knees, rocking backwards and forwards with his shoulders bobbing up and down. Wee Dave approached Slyme and put his hand on his back.

'Come on Slyme, it's just a game,' he muttered.

When Slyme looked up he replied through sniffling gasps.

'Leave,' sniffle.

'Me,' sniffle.

'Alone.'

After this he buried his head between his knees and more sniffling erupted.

Wee Dave had always been angry after defeat, but never to this extent. He felt Slyme's pain and it made him feel bad that it was he who had inflicted it.

'Let me help you with your bag,' Wee Dave whispered and started to gather his stuff, which had been kicked across the floor.

'Thanks,' Slyme mumbled when Wee Dave had finished and sat beside him. 'You played really well today.'

'So did you,' Wee Dave replied, and he wasn't lying either.

'You're making fun of me, you killed me out there.'

'But you did the same to me yesterday, remember?' Wee Dave responded. 'And the week before, and the week before…'

Slyme began picking at his shoes, and because he didn't respond Wee Dave continued, 'Those boys are beastly, we should complain to old man Stout about them. I saw one of them today picking his nose as I ran straight past him, I mean what chance have we got when a seven-year-old is picking his nose!? When I scored I looked back at him, and I swear it was so far up there I could see his fingernail at the bottom of his eye.'

Slyme looked up and Wee Dave thought he noticed a little smile appear at one corner of his mouth, so he persisted.

'Last week, when I tried to get Fooley to tackle you, he looked at me and when he smiled, his teeth were full of those little black stones. It looked like a bowl of Coco Pops.'

After this the two boys were rolling with laughter, trying to catch their breath.

They tried to stop but each time one caught the other's eye it made them start to smile, reminding them of the Coco Pops, which made them laugh even harder. This went on for the next thirty minutes, and by the time they got to class they had still not fully recovered and Mr Stout frowned as they came bounding out of the elevator.

The Glory Years had finished. The boys were eight years old now, and it was time to get serious.

The weekly timetable was as follows:

Time	Monday	Tuesday	Wednesday	Thursday	Friday
0900-1100	I.T.	Practical (Park)	English	Practical (Park)	Maths
1100-1200	Food	Food	Food	Food	Food
1200-1400	Society	Society	Society	Society	Society
1400-1500	Food	Food	Food	Food	Food
1500-1600	Football Rules and History	Football Medicine	Football Match (Park)	Football Psychology	Football Fitness

Raising his hand in the air was not enough for Wee Dave to catch Stout's attention. Another minute of reaching for the sky, waving his arm frantically, but no response.

'Mr Stout,' he cried, unable to hold himself any longer.

Stout raised his head from his iPad.

'Yes?' he sighed.

'Why do adults cry when they're happy?'

Another sigh. 'What do you mean?'

'I have just watched a video from a World Cup… for our History assignment, and the City team who won… well, a lot of the players held the trophy above their heads, but they were crying. Why are they so sad?'

Stout stood up and got the attention of the class.

'Now boys, how many times do I have to tell you? If you have any questions, google it. I do not want to hear another word from anyone.' He sat back in his usual position, ankles crossed on top of the table, set his iPad on his lap and was not disturbed for the rest of the day.

Wee Dave did google this but could not find any answers, many of the results being restricted or taking too long to load. He gave up and watched more videos after completing his daily exam. His eyes kept darting to the top of the screen to see the time, counting down the minutes until the final whistle.

Boredom, oh so boring, video after video, exam after exam, assignment after assignment, Google, Google, Google... Screen too bright, eyes in pain, so much pain, constant headaches. He squeezed his thumb and middle finger to the bridge of his nose trying to ease the pain. Oh, the pain. He hung his head back, looking to the ceiling, head creaking from side to side, hands gliding through his hair before being clasped behind his head, eyes closed, dreaming, dreaming... when will this end? Why won't this end?

'Simon!' Stout called. 'Can you come down here please?'

Wee Dave opened his eyes, stared at the ceiling for a moment before turning his head to the right to see Simon, who was shaking all the way to the bottom.

'With your iPad, Simon!' Stout howled.

Wee Dave puffed his cheeks and after grabbing Simon's iPad, he passed it to him and whispered, 'Don't worry, you'll be okay.'

After pounding himself in the forehead three times, Simon thanked him.

'Thank you.'

'Thank you.'

'Thank you.'

'It's okay Simon, go on down and see Stout,' Wee Dave pleaded.

'Thank you.' Waving his iPad in the air. 'Thank you.'

'Thank you.'

'Simon!' Stout demanded. 'Let's go.'

Simon began descending the steps, still saying 'thank you' to no one in particular.

The class dropped their eyes, nobody wanting to look up… hush, quiet, silence, the calm before…

'YOU HAVE THE SAME INFORMATION AS EVERYONE ELSE, IF YOU ARE UNABLE TO COMPLETE THE TASK AT HAND, YOU ARE NOT TRYING HARD ENOUGH!'

Wee Dave had a lot of sympathy for Simon, who clearly had difficulties studying like the rest of the class, but who was he to say anything? Wee Dave had learned very early in his School career that the students should keep quiet and concentrate on themselves.

The subject which Wee Dave hated the most was Society.

'Society. The most important part of our lives today,' began Mr Stout in the first lesson. 'If you want to be a good person in today's society, you must work your way up the ladder and earn lots of money. This is the only way you can be happy.'

Mr Stout had a habit of taking a long pause at the end of each sentence to catch his breath, and this made some of class snigger because it sounded more like a snore.

'Many years ago we had a divided society,' he grunted, 'where we all interacted with each other, no matter the race, nationality or class.'

Pause and snore.

'These were horrific times, when there was non-stop war and destruction.'

Mr Stout took a slurp from his mug, shaking his head in disapproval.

'The leader of the time, the great Mr Smite, was able to fix this. The bad people were weeded out and now we have our City back, where the citizens live in peace and happiness. Upperton, where I live, is the ultimate success story.'

Pause and snore.

'The people who live here do so because they have worked hard for their entire lives, wanting to achieve the biggest and best things. The people here deserve to be superior to the rest.'

At the next snort, a circle of light crossed the room as Stout exaggerated the movement of his wrist to have a look at his shiny golden watch. Holding it there for a second too long, he raised his eyebrows and exhaled slowly before continuing.

'Lowerton...' Mr Stout shook his head and let out another long sigh. 'If you do not work hard, this is where you will end up. Have a look at the front page of the *Bull Standard* today.'

The sound of sliding doors could be heard across the classroom, followed by the ruffling of papers and then silence.

On the front page there was a hooded man standing in the middle of a street, back to the camera with his arms raised to the sides. Wee Dave noticed a brown and red tattoo on his calf, thinking he had seen it somewhere before. Where? He couldn't put his finger on it... In front of this man were two other men, both wearing red and brown, who seemed to be wrestling with each other. The background of the picture was a pub full of drunks, laughing and smiling.

The headline...

LOWERTON LOUTS AT IT AGAIN.

More Violence in Lowerton as grown men have too much to drink and brawl in the middle of the street.

'Terrible. Absolutely terrible,' cried Mr Stout after a few moments, looking to the heavens and shaking his head. 'This... is... the... scum... of... society,' he said, banging his fist off the table with every word.

He took another slurp from his mug and set it down rather forcefully before lowering his voice to almost a whisper.

'There are two ways you can go, two paths you can choose. Number one,' Stout raised a stubby finger. 'Work hard, become rich and live a happy life.' He paused for effect, or was it for a snort? Then raising two fingers in the air he carried on, 'Or B, be lazy and live like an animal.'

That was Society.

Practical sessions were by far everyone's favourites, reminding the class of the good old days, of the Glory Years, but Wee Dave also enjoyed learning the history and rules of the game. 'After all,' they were told, 'if you do not know the rules of football by ten years old, you have no chance of playing in the League of the Sky.'

One day a thought popped into Wee Dave's head. *I've never seen a girl playing football.* Frowning and thinking some more...all of the boys had told stories of playing football with their fathers and brothers, not sisters and mothers. So where to find the answer? Google...

'Girls never have, nor ever will play football, they have their own specialised sports.' (Mr Smite, 2020).

Hmm... there must be something else about this, Wee Dave thought, but no matter what way he asked Google, the same quote from Mr Smite kept appearing.

I know!!

Google... *OTHER AUTHORs.* Enter.

Wee Dave's eyes were blinded by the light emanating from his iPad, forming a huge red circle on the ceiling above his head. In the centre of this circle the name '*DAVID BLANCH*' was written in bold letters for all to see. The screeching of the alarm deafened the classroom as each student put their fingers to their ears, ears which were still ringing long after the alarm stopped. Wee Dave looked to Mr Stout, who was taking note of the incident, and when he returned his eyes to the iPad the red flashing letters of '*RESTRICTED. DO NOT ENTER THIS ZONE*' were across the screen. First warning for Wee Dave, two more and he's out.

Wee Dave, feeling the need to explain himself, approached Mr Stout after class.

'Um… Mr Stout,' he stammered. 'Are we not allowed to read other authors?'

Mr Stout gazed at Wee Dave, mouth open in horror.

'Why do you want to read *other* authors?'

'I would like to see a different view of the world, sir.'

Mr Stout chuckled, which sounded more like a furball had got stuck in the back of his throat, and said, 'Mr Smite has already done that for us.'

'I know,' Wee Dave persisted, 'but it would still be nice to read something different, especially what happened before Mr Smite.'

'Don't be so preposterous,' he shot back. 'You do not need to know all of this to become a football player.'

'I know, I know. I'm interested though.'

'Interested, eh? Well you needn't be. Come on boy, let's go.' And with no more comment he escorted Wee Dave up the stairs and shooed him into the elevator.

Mum was furious when she heard this story. 'Why do you want to know about the time before Mr Smite?' she raved, echoing much of what Mr Stout had already warned. Wee Dave zoned in and out of Mum ranting about 'That's the way it's always been done,' and

'You don't need to know this,' and 'Do you think you're above everyone else, these *different* views!' Becoming fed up, Wee Dave knew better than to answer back and went to his room.

After this incident, Wee Dave had no questions, accepting what was taught, knowing that completing exams without getting any more warnings was the quickest way to leave School.

It was not all doom and gloom for Wee Dave ,who had his best friend to joke with, everything from PoopaLattes to pricking Mr Stout with a pin.

'Do you reckon he would fly around the air like a balloon, or would he just blow up?' asked Slyme one day after another dull Society class.

'Nah, I think he'd collapse slowly like a parachute,' replied Wee Dave.

'Those noises he makes! He sounds like a pig that has just woke himself up with his own fart,' Slyme shot back, although the sounds of their laughter was probably more like a gang of pigs which had got together and done the same thing.

That's right, they were not the most mature of eight-year-olds, but with the exams just around the corner it was nice to relax and have fun, generally taking their minds off the normal stressful environment of an eight-year-old.

'The problem with the Lazies,' Mr Stout said, warning of the importance of the upcoming exams, 'is that they can never come back to normal class, this means that you may have to stay in School for an extra year or even two!' Not wanting to stay in School any longer, Wee Dave and Slyme buried their heads into the family iPads as soon as they got home until they went to bed.

Studying, studying, studying, studying, studying.

The stinging in his head was vicious, like someone had drilled a hole through his ear and left the screw inside. And he constantly had a black spot at the centre of his vision, stars appearing in his eyes like tiny fireworks at random moments, which made him feel dizzy. He could not sleep with the pain and this only made him worse the next day. The vicious cycle, never... ending.

Complaining to Mum and Dad of sore eyes and headaches did not help, Wee Dave was always met with the same response. 'That's School, son. We've all been there.'

Voicing his concerns to Slyme, he had an answer.

'Have one of these,' he said, holding out his hand which had a little blue disc in it.

'What is it?' frowned Wee Dave.

'It helps you concentrate. I was having the same problem about a month ago and Father sent me to the doctor. Before I started taking these, I needed to read everything two or three times for it to make sense, but now I fly through my reading and even have time to play with my soldiers before I go to bed.'

Wee Dave took the blue disc from Slyme's hand and threw it into his mouth, but it got caught at the back of his throat and he began to choke.

'You're meant to take a drink with it, silly,' Slyme said, passing his bottle to Wee Dave.

That night, when Wee Dave got home, he read through his homework in double-quick time and remembered everything as clear as day. Getting halfway down the stairs...

'Get upstairs and finish your studying!'

'I have finished,' he answered.

Dad opened his mouth in shock horror, and after a few seconds of glaring he said, 'Well… go and read it again!'

Wee Dave knew better than to argue with Dad about homework. Sighing, he returned to his room, quickly became bored, imagined life outside of School, playing in the League of the Sky, living in Upperton, having lots of money…

They're wrong, he thought, thinking of the amount of times he had heard someone say that School was the best time of your life. *It's got to get better than this!*

Chapter 4

Dave

Wee Dave ascended the last step from the dressing room and the crowd was immense, the noise deafening. Taking a deep breath, he looked around the stadium, trying to spot his mum and dad, but it was impossible. Jumping into the air a few times he tried to calm himself, but he was so excited.

My professional debut, I've made it!

Well, not yet, we've still got to get to the League of the Sky! said another part of his brain.

But this is the first step, look at this crowd! I've been dreaming of this for ages.

Wee Dave got into his position, just behind the striker.

'The most important position on the pitch, young man,' Coach Alan had told him in training that week. 'You must create chances, score goals and defend when we lose the ball. I'm not sure you're up for it but I'll give you a chance. We're only playing The Dolphins and they're useless, full of tubes, so it should be a gift for us!'

'I'll show him,' he thought, and mimicking Coach Alan. 'Not sure I'm up for it? Not sure? Just you wait.'

The shrill of the whistle signalled the start of the game. Looking for space, where is the space? Looking for space. Finding space. 'Here, here, here,' Wee Dave motioned with his hands pointing to his feet. A few more calls of 'Yeah, pass, pass, I'm open!'

Wee Dave wiped the sweat from his eyes. He felt as though he had run a marathon, but he had still not touched the ball in the first ten minutes, mainly because the defence chose to pass from side to side. He looked to the dugout. Coach Alan was remonstrating with his hands, trying to shout something, but Wee Dave could not hear a thing. Cupping his hand to his ear he could make out the faint voice but understood noth—

'Oi, Dave!! Eyes on the ball,' came the shout from one of his teammates. In all of the strain of trying to understand what Coach Alan was saying, Wee Dave had forgotten that there was a game going on and when the ball was played to him, it slowly rolled past and out of play. Coach threw his hands in the air.

'Drown out the crowd, drown out the noise, and play your own game.' Words spoken to him in a distant memory somewhere, that seemed so long ago, how I want to…

'DAVE!!!' Again the ball had been passed to him.

Right, get your act together, let's go!

Suddenly, the ball deflected into the air and Wee Dave stopped it dead with his left. A quick glance before he received the ball had told him that there was a defender close behind him, so taking his first touch in the other direction, he was gone like a whippet. A couple of stepovers took him past the next defender with relative ease, and…

Agh, just ran it out, he thought. *Next time…*

But he could not ignore the groan from the crowd.

'Best be careful, Wee Man,' Barry said. 'Gaffer does not like us losing the ball.'

Possession. Possession. Possession. What's the obsession with possession? The right way, learn to play the right way. Possession. Possession. Sideways, back, sideways, back, surely possession should be further up the field?

Frustrated, Wee Dave dropped deeper and deeper, trying to get a touch of the ball. Barry finally found him and…

Injection of speed, close control, that left foot, wow, what a left foot, stuck to it like glue, incredible.

'One–two,' Wee Dave shouted as he gave the ball to Mark and sprinted past the defender. Mark took a touch and then played his pass through. *Why not first time?* Wee Dave thought, although he was still on the end of it, one-on-one with the goalkeeper. Relaaaaax and bang… 1–0. Slotted to the side of the keeper easily. Wheeling away in celebration he thought of…

'YOU'RE OFFSIDE YOU MORON!' Coach Alan screamed. 'GET BACK AND HELP YOUR TEAM!'

If only Mark had given me the pass a little earlier.

Possession, possession, posses… Wee Dave drops to receive, injection of pace, good chance, close!!

Possession, possession, posses… Wee Dave drops to receive, injection of pace, good chance, close!!

Possessio, possession, posses… Wee Dave drops to receive, injection of pace, good chance, close!!

Possessio

Possess

Possessszzzzzzzzzzz

He would have liked to have touched the ball more but he was in the zone now, knowing he was dangerous, knowing he was creating chance after chance.

The half was petering out, still 0–0 when Wee Dave picked it up in his own half. Bursting past four players, he set it up on his left foot.

This is going top corn— aw, what a run that is!

Shaping to shoot, Wee Dave played a disguised pass through for Mark, who finally slid one past the keeper.

1–0

'Get in,' Wee Dave clenched his fist.

Coach Alan ran the length of the touchline, arms flailing before he jumped into the crowd of players on top of Mark.

Good timing for a goal, the whistle blew.

Half-time.

Wee Dave bounced into the changing room. He had played amazingly, he was the danger man, and what about that assist? Magic.

Taking their seats, the team sat in silence, waiting for Coach to come in. A glance around the changing room showed blank stares, nobody giving anything away… with the exception of one who could not keep the cheeky grin and two dimples from his face.

'Right lads,' Coach grumbled, looking at the floor. 'Absolute quality at the back, keeping the ball well, not giving them a sniff, love it.' A ripple of tension filled the changing room as some of the players gave a brief smile before returning to their poker face.

'Marko, fantastic goal son, keep it up.' Coach's words had become quieter, almost a whisper. A wave of tension now, the resounding smell of dry mud hit Wee Dave's nose, he was confused that those around him were not smiling but they knew... they knew what was coming.

A moment's silence, Coach lifted his head.

A tsunami.

'YOU,' he bellowed, pointing directly at Wee Dave. 'CAN YOU NOT HEAR ME OUT THERE? ARE YOU DEAF?'

'Whh-wh-whhat?' he stammered.

'Well, you must be deaf if you can't even hear me in here,' he threatened. 'You've lost the ball almost every single time. Why are you going forward when it is not on?'

It was now Wee Dave's turn to pick a point on the floor.

'You can't keep giving the ball away, you are in a professional league now, no mistakes allowed,' he growled. Wee Dave's heart, oh the heartbeat, his lower lip trembling with the heartbeat.

Bearing down on him, Coach yelled, 'LOOK AT ME WHEN I'M SPEAKING TO YOU, BOY!'

Wee Dave raised his puppy eyes, no good here.

'You've got ten minutes to show me that you are good enough for this team. If you're not up to it, you can get out,' he said, pointing his thumb through the door.

After leaving through said door, a fly on the wall would have thought the team were at a funeral.

Dave puffed his cheeks before stepping out for the second half, even more anxious than he was at the beginning of the game. He wiped a final tear from his eye and took another breath.

Come on, stop feeling sorry for yourself, he thought. *Coach is trying to improve me, that's why he's shouting.*

Remembering the days when he first started, setting himself new challenges: this is the same.

I'll keep possession, I'll show Coach!

He did a few high bounces into the air. *Come on! Come on! Come on! Let's go! Let's go! I'm lucky to be here, lucky to be playing under a great coach!*

The rest of the team were already on the field when Dave took his position.

'Let's keep the ball better this half, lads,' Mark shouted, clapping his hands together and keeping his eye firmly on Dave. Dave would not let the team down!

Whistle. Noise. Space. Possession.

Possession, Dave, possession, Dave, possession.

Dave knew he could have taken the ball on himself, created some chances, but possession was the key. Ten minutes into the second half, Dave had touched the ball twenty-three times, and had 100% pass completion. Perfect, exactly what Coach…

The ball deflected out for a goal kick, the board had risen.

Dave, your number is up, Dave your time is up. Oh Dave, Dave, what have you done?

What have I done?

'Did I do okay, Coach?' he asked, but Coach either did not hear him or chose to ignore him.

Dave was downbeat, but hey, he had just made his professional debut, made a great assist, had 100% pass completion in the second half. All in all, pretty decent debut. But how boring, being on the bench, oh… a football!

Wee Dave grabbed it, and began to practise some keepy-ups and skill moves.

'How can you improve prancing around with that ball?' Coach demanded. 'Sit on that bench and watch the game!' Dave sat down. Dave did as he was told.

Dave could hear Coach's commands from here, seemingly a conveyor belt of 'PASS, THAT WAY, SPACE, PASS, PASS, PASS.' Oh how boring, boring watching, he wanted to be out there playing. Boredom, snooooooozzzeee.

He was brought back to his senses by the final whistle.

'Good 3–0 win, grab your bottles and come in to me,' Coach ordered.

The team gathered in a circle around Coach, who was going through the game, saying that they had done this well, how they could improve on that blah blah blah, mostly a load of nonsense...

'Dave, stay behind for a moment.'

'Sure.'

The team waved their goodbyes and Coach put his hand on Dave's shoulder, locking him to the spot.

'Listen, son, you are going to have to work hard to get into this team. We were unbeaten last year, we won everything, there is no way I am going to risk that, do you understand?'

'Yes, Coach.'

'That first half was ridiculous, you gave the ball away so many times and we can't be having that in this team. Okay?'

'Okay, Coach.'

'The second half was even worse!'

Confusion. Silence. What to say?

'You were in some really good positions to get forward and score a goal, yet you decided to pass back. What were you thinking?'

Dave dropped his head, the body odour and devil eyes from Coach Alan were too much for him to take, he knew he was going to well up at any moment but fought bravely to keep it in.

'I know it was your debut and you were probably nervous, so I'll cut you some slack. But you need to get yourself to training and to do everything I say.'

'Okay, Coach,' and with that, Dave's shoulder was free.

Dad was beaming with pride when Dave trudged to the car.

'You were fantastic out there, son. Did you enjoy yourself? A win on your debut, you must have had the time of your life!'

'Yeah, it was great,' Dave replied in monotone.

'Great? Great? It was much better than great. You have a massive career ahead of you young man, you can count yourself lucky.'

'I suppose so.'

Dad did not shut his mouth all the way home, about how his son would do this and how his son would do that. Dave still felt terrible for the way he had played throughout the match, he had given the ball away so many times in the first half and did not attack in the second. No matter how much praise Dad was giving him, he only cared about what Coach Alan thought. After all, he was qualified, he had experience, he knew how to get players to the League of the Sky.

The sky grew dark, where were the football clouds?

Dave, where are the football clouds?

Chapter 5

Charity Match

One Friday, to the surprise of Wee Dave, Dad was waving from his car after school. Usually Mum did the driving.

'Is everything okay, Dad?' asked Wee Dave, opening the passenger door.

'Of course Son, today you're gonna watch me play football,' he answered.

'What for?' Wee Dave replied, offending Dad without meaning to.

'Well… it's a charity match for a friend of mine,' Dad said. 'Some good footballers come here you know, you'll love it!'

'You play football?'

'Not so much anymore, but I did when I was younger.'

'Oh..' Silence, no interest, no cares for Wee Dave.

'Anyway,' Dad tried again, 'you know the buildings in 10/10?' Wee Dave glanced out of the window where he could see the unmistakable buildings from the centre of Middleton, all the same size, same shape, same brown and white colour, same same same. The only difference being the wording along the sides.

'Yes.' Boredom. Just... want... to... play... football.

'Did you know that I helped to build them?'

Oh...

'Really?' Wee Dave answered in a surprised tone, raising his head like a meerkat to get a better look. It had never occurred to Wee Dave that these buildings were not always there.

'Yes,' Dad laughed. 'This match is in remembrance for the builders who lost their lives.'

Wee Dave was intrigued. 'What happened to them?'

'Some of them fell to their deaths, some got hit in the head by falling bricks... they were the lucky ones.'

Wee Dave frowned.

'What do you mean, lucky?'

'Well... I was really privileged. Before we started on these buildings, I had just finished School, and that meant I could get a job at the Bank once the work was complete.'

Dad let out a sigh and then continued in a serious tone.

'Thousands of kids were taken out of School as there was a lot of work to do in such a short space of time. It was brilliant, all the young lads getting real money, helping their families live a normal life... and that they did. They did live normal lives. But as soon as the work was complete most of the builders could not find another job, and by then they were too old to return to School. So the majority ended up on the streets, begging for survival.'

Wee Dave, thanks to the 'most important topic' in School, was well aware that money made the world spin, that without money no one can survive, that he had to keep working hard in School, he had to work hard for Society, otherwise he would end up with no money and be unhappy for the rest of his days.

'Mr Stout has told us about beggars,' Wee Dave said matter-of-factly. 'He says they are very bad people and we should stay away from them.'

'There are a few things that School will not teach you, son, and this is one of them,' Dad stated. 'Beggars are still people, just like me and you and Mum and Mr Stout, the only difference is they struggle to find work through no fault of their own. Most of them have been very unlucky, in the wrong place at the wrong time.'

They sat in silence for the next few minutes, until Dad brought them back to the subject of the charity match.

'Listen, son, it is hard to explain what this match is about but it means a lot to me. A builder friend of mine was one of the unfortunate ones, he could not find a job, he had no money, nothing... so he became a beggar.' Dad let out a cough before continuing.

'A few years after the building work was complete he had a kid, about the same age as you, and he begged for money, for help, for himself and for his family. He came to our house. Knocked... begged.'

Dad paused as the traffic lights changed from red to green, putting the car into drive before going on. Wee Dave sat in a daydream, not knowing what to say but wanting to find out what happened.

'You've got to understand that your mum and I were not in the greatest position ourselves. You had just been born, so Mum was out of work, and I was earning minimum wage at the Bank, so we could not help him.'

Dad stopped talking as he slowed the car to let an old man cross.

'About a month after his first visit he returned, dressed in the same clothes but they were covered in filth and ripped to shreds. He held his hands out but didn't have the energy to say anything.'

This poor man, thought Wee Dave, *how could Dad let his friend come to this? Or was it Dad's fault?*

'He didn't even remember who I was! I mean, we were best friends for years, just like you and that Slyme kid. I did not realise things had got so...' Dad wiped a tear and cleared his throat.

'I took him to Hospital here in Middleton, but of course you need medical insurance and the doctors would not see him. So I quickly rushed across to Lowerton where I found a hospital, but the waiting line was out the door, and I mean the line was two blocks long. There was nothing else we could do but wait.'

Dad stopped explaining as unbearable silence ensued.

'Did he die, Dad?'

'Yes... we had been waiting for over an hour when he died in my arms. We didn't even get to the door,' Dad sobbed and wiped a tear with the sleeve of his jacket.

'That was nine years ago, just after you were born, and on the anniversary of his death the builders and other ex-pros get together for a match, with all of the proceeds going to the scum and the beggars. Starvation is the biggest killer in the City and 100% of it is in Lowerton, so we try our best to help.'

'Did he like football?'

'Did he? He could do anything with the ball, the only player I've ever seen who could control a ball that was thrown from the tops of the buildings in 10/10. He'd take it down on his chest, keep it up a few times and then volley it back up. The stuff that man could do was incredible!'

Wee Dave's jaw dropped as he looked out the window and squinted to see the tops of the buildings in the distance. Surely not!

'We were the best team in the City before the League of the Sky took over,' Dad reminisced.

'You played for the best team in the City?' Wee Dave blurted.

Dad laughed. 'Don't be so surprised, I was a decent wee player, I mean I've put a bit of beef on in the last number of years, but I can still play.'

'You're not as fat as Stout or Slyme!' Wee Dave retorted.

'I'm not exactly Mr Fitness though, am I?' Dad said with a sly grin. 'Listen, I know you love your football, a lot more than I did when I was your age, so you'll enjoy today.'

He stopped talking and Wee Dave realised that they were getting close to the bridge.

'Are we going to Lowerton, Dad?' he muttered, starting to feel frightened. 'What about the violence?' The *Bull Standard* still reported new crimes every day.

'We are going there to help these people, son, they're not going to hurt us,' Dad reassured him, but Wee Dave's heart was hammering, he did not like going into the unknown. Who does?

After crossing the river on the old grey bridge which separated Middleton and Lowerton, Wee Dave looked out of the window and saw high tower after high tower, more and more of them as far as the eye could see.

Middleton and Lowerton had the same chessboard outline, with the two Main Streets running through the centre to form a cross from a bird's-eye view. The two main streets of Middleton were for transport only, usually to the ten mile square of 10/10 located in the centre. Outside of 10/10, the streets were filled to the perimeter with brown-bricked terraced houses, each with a backyard but no front. Same same same...

On the contrary, the people of Lowerton, better known as scum or beggars, lived on one of the two mains streets which formed a gigantic cross on the perfectly square outline. Outside of this cross was mostly wasteland. And the high tower after high tower on the centre cross of Lowerton was the only thing Wee Dave could see.

'It's a bit old school here, isn't it, son? The people here live in these buildings.'

'What? Don't be ridiculous, they are massive.'

'Oh no,' Dad chuckled, 'these are called apartments. There are probably around 200 different families living in each building.'

'So there are 200 people living inside one building?' Absurd!

'No, son,' Dad answered. 'There are a hell of a lot more than that. There are maybe six or seven people in each family... so you're talking over a thousand.'

Wee Dave looked to the horizon, trying to calculate how many people lived here. Too many!

At a set of traffic lights Dad took a turn to the left, and they were met with a tunnel of overhanging trees, leaves floating to the ground to form a beautiful brown and red carpet. The gaps in between the trees created a fascinating shadow, which looked like a descending ladder as they drove through wasteland.

Wee Dave had been exposed to some of the dazzling gardens of Middleton, but he had never seen trees as big as this and he cherished the natural beauty before his eyes. When Dad stopped the car and said, 'We're here,' Wee Dave thought he had lost his mind.

There were no football buildings in sight!

Following his Dad, they slushed their way through another narrower tree tunnel and after a few minutes they came to an opening. Underneath them, inside what was the shape of a giant oval bowl, was a football pitch. It was not the bowl or the size of the pitch that surprised Wee Dave.

'Dad, is that real grass?'

'When I was your age, all football was played on grass,' Dad sniggered. 'Actually, that's a lie, we used to play on the road as well.'

'Seriously? Did you not get sick?'

'No,' Dad laughed and ruffled Wee Dave's hair. 'You young 'uns don't know how lucky you are, getting the pitches you do.'

On the field there were grown men in little groups, passing the ball around with one player in the middle trying to defend. Others were passing to each other at different angles and distances.

They're not playing normal football!

'What are they doing?' Wee Dave said, pointing.

'They're warming up.'

Wee Dave showed no sign of understanding, so Dad rolled his eyes and continued.

'They do this to get ready for the real match. My word, David, what are they teaching you in that School?'

'Mostly about Society and money. How successful people in the League of the Sky are heroes and...'

Dad cut him off.

'And what happens to the people who don't make it to the League of the Sky?'

Wee Dave was dumbfounded. In all of his excitement at being one of the best players in School, he had never thought of *not* playing in the League of the Sky.

The silence obviously answered Dad's question, because he continued. 'The majority of people who go to that School do not have a career in football. You'll figure it out as you get older, but money rules the game, in fact money rules the City, and for people like us living in Middleton… it's going to take a hell of a good player to get into the top league.'

Dad was frustrated. What was School doing for those who would not make a career in football? What was School doing for the majority?

Wee Dave found the spectators more interesting that the football on show. They were dotted around the concrete, enjoying a beer and a burger while chatting about their lives, at times singing songs and the whole time laughing and smiling. Wee Dave found it strange seeing people's faces and not the tops of their heads.

Bringing his eyes back to the boring game, one of the players had a shot which went wildly over the crossbar. Behind the goal, a kid… a kid playing football, practising keepy-ups. Wee Dave stared for five minutes and the ball had not dropped. Wow!

Creeping closer, he realised that the ball was actually a bundle of empty chip bags and the juggles were being performed with no shoes, just bare feet. The kid was skinny and pale, had bright blue eyes, curly blond hair just over the ears under a little flat cap. The clothes were too small… they were filthy and frazzled.

The kid lofted the ball towards Wee Dave and shouted, 'Two touches.' Wee Dave caught this muddy excuse for a football, not knowing what else to do.

'You're meanta control and pass back, ya eejit.'

'Oh, sorry,' Wee Dave replied.

'No worries,' the kid said, and started to punch the palm of the other hand. 'Just don't mess up next time, or else.'

Wee Dave was stunned. *Is he going to punch me? Why? Because I won't give him his ball? Yeah, that's probably it. Throw it back to him… Throw it, throw it. Do something!* Wee Dave was frozen to the spot.

'The name's Jamie,' the kid said, taking off the flat cap to reveal a mop of blond shaggy hair, then holding out a hand with a smile which stretched from ear to ear.

'Wee Dave,' he replied, returning the handshake. Jamie's handshake was so strong that Wee Dave thought he was going to lose his fingers.

'State of these ol' farts tryna play footie,' Jamie nodded in the direction of the match.

'I know, I was up on that hill there watchin', but I fell asleep,' Wee Dave answered, trying to make himself sound cool.

'What's yer team?'

Wee Dave stumbled for an answer. *My team?* he thought.

'I'm a Buccaneers man meself. You know… Come on the Mighty Masses of the Needy.' Jamie started to sing a song and then frowned as he was met with silence. 'You know… The Buccaneer Falls? The Brown and Red Pirates. The best team in all of the land.'

Wee Dave knew he was talking nonsense because School had taught him that the City was the greatest team, they had the richest history, the best players and most importantly, the most money. As well as this, Slyme always wore the red-and-white uniform, and Slyme knew more about football than anyone.

'You're wrong, the best team in the world is the City.'

'You're nat from round here, are ye? Where ye from?' Jamie asked.

'Middleton,' Wee Dave blurted.

'Ah right, that explains. You bais are clueless 'bout footie,' he said rolling his eyes. 'Me Granda always says that. He brings me to The Buccaneers every week, you should hear the noise, different gravy mate, much better than that muck you watch on TV. You ever been?'

'No,' Wee Dave mumbled, looking to the ground and kicking the grass. He was beginning to feel a little out of his depth.

'Nah, wouldn'a thought so. Don' understand what yer talking 'bout then.'

How to answer? What to do? Nothing. Silence.

'You play?' Jamie asked, changing the subject.

'Yes.'

'Any good?'

'The best in School.' Slyme was probably still better, but Wee Dave wanted to impress Jamie.

'Fancy a game then?'

'Definitely,' Wee Dave said with enthusiasm, there was no way Jamie was going to beat him. 'When?'

'Right nigh.'

Wee Dave frowned in confusion, where would they play? They had no football and Wee Dave had no kit, he had no football boots.

Jamie nodded towards the field. 'Unless you wanna watch that pile o' dung?'

Wee Dave glanced over in disapproval, shrugged his shoulders and answered, 'Definitely not! Let's go.'

'Right, go make posts down there,' Jamie said, pointing to nowhere in particular, 'and I'll do the other goal.'

'What do you mean?' How could he make a goal appear from thin air?

Jamie tutted, rolled his eyes to the sky and said, 'You Middle City bais, clueless!' After running up the oval bank, Jamie returned with four twigs and began to twist one into the ground. A few feet to the side, same again. Posts!

Ahhh, I see. Wee Dave understood and trotted to the other side to plug his goals in.

'First to ten?' Wee Dave shouted, rubbing his hands from the dirt of the twig.

'Aye, no sweat,' Jamie shouted back. 'Here, you start.' Jamie kicked the ball into the air and it landed straight on Wee Dave's foot.

Come on, just like in School, Wee Dave thought, but he was struggling, he could not kick the empty chip bags out of his feet, it did not roll like a ball, the grass was uneven, bumpy and he fell to the ground, the grass, the dirt, so dirty, disgusting. He looked from the ground to Jamie, to the bag, and back to Jamie.

He's laughing at me!

Of course he is, look at the state of you, lying on the ground, get up!

Failure after failure.

This is impossible. Absolutely impossible. Nobody can play like this.

Persistence.

Right, here we go, it's in front of me, I'm seeing the bumps, avoiding them, I'm getting close.

BANG!

Jamie came storming out of the goal like a bull, shoved Wee Dave, took the ball and in the blink of an eye it was 1–0.

'That's a foul,' Wee Dave shouted from the ground, the stink of the mud catching in the back of his throat.

Laughing, Jamie returned to the goal and with a tap of the shoulder said, 'Shoulder to shoulder mate.'

'But I fell to the ground,' Wee Dave moaned.

'So?'

'When someone falls over you stop the game!' raged Wee Dave.

He watched in utter despair as Jamie fell to the floor, crying with laughter.

'Granda's gonna love that one,' Jamie said, still hunched over, trying to catch a breath.

The laughter had a calming effect on Wee Dave, seeing this kid roll on the ground, the funny accent. Everything about Jamie made Wee Dave smile, that smile was contagious. A smile is contagious. There are no smiles in Middleton, only the top of everyone's noggin. Smile, be happy. Jamie's laughter was not evil, not like when Slyme had beaten him, it was genuine joy, genuine happiness.

'In School we stop the game when someone falls over, just in case they are hurt,' Wee Dave explained.

'And are they ever injured?'

Wee Dave thought about this, the number of times the game had been stopped, stop, start, stop, start. Very annoying, especially when he was about to unleash his left foot. In fact, more and more time in the Park was spent waiting on people getting off the ground, rather than just playing. Play, remember the days of play. The Glory Years…

'Never,' Wee Dave confirmed

'Aye, thought so,' pronounced Jamie. '1–0.'

The next three goals were the same. *I'm so weak, so weak. How could I have thought…?*

Shut up, get your act together.

He's too good, what's the point?

Just be stronger, faster, keep trying.

Pushing off the ground, mud all over his hands, he gave them a wipe on his T-shirt and looked at Jamie, whose smile had not faded.

'Right, bring it on!'

He started to dribble forwards again… 5–0. AAAAARRRGGGHHHHHH!!!!

There was a glimmer of hope, though. Rather than whimper away, he had at least struggled for the ball. Again...

6–0, keep going! thought Wee Dave. Though Wee Dave was getting hammered, he could feel the improvement each time and he promised himself not to give up until Jamie had scored the winning goal.

In the next play, Wee Dave caught up with Jamie and got a toe on the ball. As Jamie fell to the ground, Wee Dave quickly got the ball under control and was bearing down on goal. Just as he was about to let loose with his left foot, Jamie's leg came out of nowhere, touched the ball to the side and Wee Dave volleyed the leg.

That is definitely broken, thought Wee Dave, *it must be!* But as Wee Dave was mulling this over in his head, Jamie was up off the ground and... 7–0

'I thought your leg...' Wee Dave began.

'Takes a lat more than that to keep me down! But here... that was some battlin'. Keep it up!'

Both players gave their all to score the next goal. Shirts were tugged, ankles kicked, knees chopped, shoulders barged, nothing would keep them down. Last gasp tackle from Jamie, counter-attack, a lunge from Wee Dave, counter-attack. It was nip and tuck, neck and neck, a toenail being just enough to win the ball/bag.

Suddenly, Wee Dave had an edge, he was a hair's breadth in front, sweat stinging his eyes, the hot breath of Jamie on the back of his neck, as he was pulling his shirt, strangling him, strangled, he's being choked out, falling backwards, falling, backwards, eyes to the sky... but with one final breath, with one final lunge, he got his toenail to the ball. The two players fell to the ground and watching in disbelief, his heart stopped, the world stopped, but the ball slowly bounced between the two sticks.

7–1. Pure elation for Wee Dave.

YEEEEEEAAAASSSS!!! He put his arms out by his sides and like an airplane, wheeled away in celebration with his eyes to the sky. Where did he get the energy? By the time Wee Dave brought his eyes back to the earth, it was too late... 8–1.

'Ah, come on,' Wee Dave moaned.

Jamie winked and smiled, 'No rest in this game.'

Ten minutes later the game was over, 10–4. His heart was pumping, he was gasping for air, pain was in every bone and every muscle of his body, his legs were heavy, his arms heavier, it felt like his whole body was being was sucked to the ground. He was drenched in sweat, beads tickling the side of his head as it dripped down. What a game! What excitement! Wiping the sweat from his forehead and the stinging from his eyes, Wee Dave looked to the skies, looked to the football clouds which were surrounding him. He turned his head and watched Jamie go through the same motions.

After a minute or so Jamie turned to the side and with hand resting on head asked, 'New game?'

'Definitely, but it'll be a different story this time.' Wee Dave grinned, the dimples in his cheeks deeper than they had ever been.

'Sure, I'm only playing at 50%,' Jamie said. 'I'm giving you a wee bitta hope.'

Although the second game lasted a lot longer and was much more competitive, Jamie still won 10–3. Wee Dave played amazingly at the start, even taking the lead, but in the end he got tired whereas Jamie seemed to get stronger.

'You're not human, mate,' Wee Dave said, trying to catch his breath. He was dead to the world but on the contrary Jamie sauntered towards him, the bags they were using for a ball safely tucked under his right arm.

'Tell you wha',' Jamie replied, 'that was tough enough mate, the scoreline didn't reflect the game. After watchin' ye prance around at the start like a ballet dancer, I had no hope for ye.'

Wee Dave took this as a compliment and smiled. 'How do you get so good?'

'S'pose it's just natural, I play about four hours a day.' Wee Dave found this remark a little strange and thought, *If I had the chance to play four hours a day, surely I'd be as good as Jamie.*

'Four hours!? What about School? What about homework?'

The smile disappeared from Jamie's face, the bright blue eyes lost their sparkle.

'Sure, we don't get much edication down here in oul Lowerton. Granda says the gov'ment don't wan' folk like us to know fings.'

Wee Dave had no reply so he just sat in silence.

After a moment Jamie's smile reappeared, the glitter came back to the eyes. 'Sure, what do I care, I'm just gonna play footie for the rest o' me life.'

At this, the final whistle blew in the charity match and Wee Dave said his goodbyes, not before Jamie told him to 'dust yerself off'. Sure enough, Wee Dave looked down at his clothes and he was a mess. Mum had always warned him about how he'd get ill if he got too dirty, so he tried to brush the dirt off but this seemed to make it worse.

Mum's going to kill me! he thought.

Chapter 6

Judgement Days

The pain in his head would not leave, that stinging pain as if someone had taken a sledgehammer to it, a constant buzz in his ears with any other noise from the outside world distracting him. He could hear his mum's voice in the distance.

Shut up!

Tweet, tweet, tweet. The birds chirping outside. Tweet, tweet, never ending.

Shut up!

Engines driving by, horns honking.

Shut up!

When the rain picked up, hammering against the window, Wee Dave slammed his book shut and closed his eyes as tight as he could. He then dug the palms of both hands into his eyes, pushing as far as he could, heaving at his eyes.

If I squash them hard enough it will get rid of the pain in my head! This pain has to go! It must leave! GET OUT!!!

Mum knocked on the door and peeked in. 'Dinner's ready, son, do you want it now or do you wanna heat it up later?'

'I'll have it now, I need a break.'

Leaning back in his chair and clasping his fingers behind his head, he stared at the mountain of books – mountain of mess more like, some books open, others closed, pages all over the place and pens not to be found anywhere – he thought of the upcoming exams. *Fail these and another year for you… 90% pass, no less.*

Standing up, he looked in the mirror. His hair was sticking up on the left side of his head, where he had been resting his hand, and after giving it a quick shuffle he looked like an old scientist. Crazy old scientist. He flattened his hair and walked closer to the mirror, studying the bags under his eyes, his eyes, his bloodshot eyes, red spider webs running through them. He closed them to rest for a second…

'David, I thought you wanted this!' Mum's voice.

Where is that coming from? Where am I?

Opening his eyes, he found himself still standing in front of the mirror, and after looking at his watch he realised he had been standing there for over ten minutes. He shook himself awake and slapped his face, leaving a huge red hand mark.

I'm so pale, he thought and as he poked at his face, red blotches appeared which slowly faded to white. *And my skin… it's on fire!*

A splash of water later and he was down at the table, eating on his own since Mum and Dad had already finished their food. This left him to his thoughts…

I hate this! Why can't I just play football?

Come on, get through these exams and you'll definitely make a team next season.

It's so hard though, my head is always sore, I feel horrendous, surely the air will do me good.

You must get your 90%, remember, or you'll have to do it all over again.

Yeah, that's the last thing I want. I miss football so much.

He thought of the last few games he had played against Slyme at the Park, their rivalry growing week by week. The games were fun and ferocious, both giving their all and challenging themselves to the extreme. Wee Dave loved it but he worried that Slyme was losing heart, as Wee Dave had become stronger and was winning more often.

Wee Dave hated Stout now, constantly interrupting practice to give demands and directions. Stop. Start. Stop. Start. Stop. Start.

Just let us play! Please just let us play! How can we learn if you're constantly gabbing?

'We've got this far without any of his help!' Wee Dave said to Slyme after one particular practice. 'Why does he need to interfere now?'

'Dad says he's only trying to help us get into a team,' Slyme replied. 'He said we should listen to any advice that he gives.'

'I know, but what advice is he giving us?' Wee Dave retorted, his face turning red with anger. 'The other day I was through on goal and he shouted at me to SHOOT! What else was I gonna do!?'

'Yeah, I saw that. Stupid innit?' Slyme said. He had become used to Wee Dave's rants so he knew it was best to agree.

'That wasn't even the worst of it. When I went over after scoring, do you know what he said to me?'

'No,' Slyme answered.

Wee Dave puffed out his belly and cheeks to imitate Stout, then started to wag his finger with every word, taking wheezy exaggerated breaths every few seconds.

'Listen – *grunt, grunt* – you'll go far – *grunt, grunt* – if you listen to me.'

He returned to his own voice and without hesitation shouted, 'What a moron, why would he say something like that? "You'll go far if you listen to me…" What does that even mean?'

Sitting in reflection of his conversations and games with Slyme, he realised that they were not getting him anywhere. Slyme only wanted to pass his exams and get to the next stage of School, he did not seem to care as much about football, and who was Wee Dave to say any better?

But Dad… Could he not convince Dad that he needed some fresh air? That he needed to be outside, playing football?

He dropped his knife and fork to the plate, looking at his half eaten dinner as memories of a conversation from a month ago came to him…

'I wish I could go back to Lowerton and play with Jamie.'

'Son, you have no time to go there I'm afraid, your exams are just around the corner,' Dad said.

'But Dad, I also have the try-outs, which are just as important if I want to play in the League of the Sky. It's the only way I can improve, if I'm playing against players who are good. The School games are boring now, they're too easy and I'm getting worse.'

'I understand, son, which is why you must study hard and pass the exams, you don't want to be in with the Lazies, do you?'

'No Dad, but I still want to improve my game.'

'It's only a few more months and then you'll be joining an academy, I'm sure of it. You're nearly ten, almost a grown-up, and you must grind and work your way through a lot of things in life. If you can, you'll be a better person for it!'

'I'll be a better player if I can play against Jamie every day,' Wee Dave mumbled in reply. 'He told me he plays four hours per day!'

'I'll tell you what, if you study hard for the next few months, I promise we'll go to Lowerton and find Jamie. How does that sound?'

Wee Dave thought for a moment and realised that this was probably the best option for him.

'You promise?'

'Yes. Now go and finish you're studying, and let's not talk of this anymore.'

Looking at his half eaten dinner plate he slid the chair back, knowing the time had come to finish his mountain of homework. On the way through the living room Mum mumbled something but he did not reply, trudging up the stairs and into his room. On the way to his mountain he looked at the calendar. These had been the longest four months of his life but it was only three weeks until the end of February, the end of exam time. He stared at that date, not taking his eyes off it.

Maybe if I stare, it will come quicker. He had tried this every day without success, if anything it made the date seem further away, so returning to his table, he flicked open to the page he had slammed shut just fifteen minutes earlier, and knowing he had no time to waste he was lost in Mr Smite's *A Brief History of the City*.

The school calendar runs from May to February. Before Smite's time, school was from September to June, but it changed because people who were born in June had an unfair advantage to those who were born in July. Now, the oldest kids in School were born in March and the youngest in February; 'A fantastic change which has made society a better place, eliminating the unfair rules from before,' according to Smite Jr, the Prime Minister of today, who was born 3 March 2014.

The football season is slightly different. Before Smite, the league was played along the same timeline as the School year; however, the age difference was done by year, meaning kids who were born in December were eleven months behind those who were born in January, eleven months of physical development, eleven months of mental development, how unfair to players who were born in December… To combat this, Mr Smite and the Head of the Football Federation, Mr Sky, changed the season to what it is today, beginning in April and finishing in January, the oldest players being born in March and the youngest in February, therefore 'eliminating the unfair and divided society that had tarnished football for years', as stated by Sky Jr, presently the Head of the Football Federation, who was born 5 March 2013.

Wee Dave passed his exams with flying colours, which qualified him to try out for a team next season. But he needed practice, he had hardly kicked a ball in anger in the last few months and he did not forget his dad's promise.

'Exams are over, Dad… Do you remember?' he asked, praying to Smite that he had not forgotten.

'Okay, son, let's go.' Dad rolled his eyes before grabbing his coat and keys.

In the car, Wee Dave was chomping at his fingernails, teeth grinding teeth as he tried to get that last little bit of fingernail, but it was hanging on for dear life – ah he's gone too far, now ripping through skin.

They arrived and Wee Dave sprung out of his seat like a greyhound from the traps, forgetting the impossible task of his fingernails and sprinting down the tree-lined path. How could he forget that path? The path he had dreamt of every night? But when he got to the end of the path and saw the oval grey bowl, grass football pitch in the middle... it was empty, not a soul in sight.

'Don't worry, son, maybe he'll turn up soon,' Dad said, arriving not long after Wee Dave and noticing the disappointment in his son's face.

'But he said he was here every day. Four hours! Where could he be?' It was 3 p.m. and Jamie did say that he did not go to School. Betrayal, why would he lie?

'I'll tell you what, why don't we play against each other? Just like the old days.'

It had been a long time since Wee Dave had played against Dad, the novelty of beating him every week had worn off because he realised that Dad was much bigger, stronger, faster and better than he was and it was obvious that he was letting Wee Dave win.

Dad sensed his hesitation...

'Okay, maybe you don't want to play against an old fart like me, why don't you practise free kicks? I've got targets we can tie onto the crossbar and we'll see if you can hit them. What do you think?'

'Alright then,' Wee Dave mumbled without any enthusiasm.

Dad reached into his bag, pulling out hoops which he tied to the top corners of the goal.

'I used to do this all the time,' he smiled. 'The best free kick taker in the City at one point.'

'Yeah?' Wee Dave replied, feigning some sort of interest. 'Yeah sure, well done, good for you, whatever.'

Wee Dave set the ball down, took a few steps back, to the side, looked at the ball, looked at the target, back to the ball, stepping in and strike!!

Not even close.

'Not as easy as it looks, eh?' Dad said. 'Here, gimme a go.'

From the same place Dad smashed one through the hoop, not even touching the sides.

How… Wee Dave tried to gasp, but he was in so much shock at how fast the ball moved, like a rocket. *How?*

'How did you do that?' he was able to blurt when a smiling Dad came back from the goal, ball safely tucked under one arm.

'Practice, son. Like I said, I came down here every day and every night to practise my free kicks on my own.'

Wee Dave had such good skills and close control that it was easy to dribble around everyone and score, he had never thought of shooting from a distance before. Why would he, if he didn't need to? But this is another part to football, if he was going to make it to the League of the Sky he knew he would have to perfect this. To be like his Dad.

He practised and practised, getting closer, closer, close, then further away, miles away. AAAAGGHH! the frustration. It took three hours before he could even kick it high enough, one shot thundering off the crossbar.

'That's it, son, you're getting closer!' Dad said from the side. These were the only words he had said since Wee Dave started to shoot.

Okay, so I've got to kick lower on the ball, and it will go higher. Wee Dave liked to figure things out for himself, he loved to experiment, it gave him a sense of achievement when a task was complete. This was the main reason he hated Stout so much, constantly directing, demanding like a PlayStation control pad.

Telling people what to do is not coaching! Guiding them and letting them figure things out for themselves… now that's a different ball game.

Wee Dave was getting closer and closer, hitting the rim of the hoop, hitting the crossbar, but in the end, he failed. Five hours and he didn't get one ball through the hoop, what a waste of time. Or was it?

'Can we come earlier tomorrow?' he asked after Dad had dragged him to the car.

'Sure, you were very good today, I know that you'll get it soon.'

They returned the next day, an hour earlier this time, and within a few minutes Wee Dave had slotted the ball through the hoop.

'Easy, eh?' Dad cheered from the side, and tongue in cheek said, 'Okay, you've done it, let's go.'

'I'm not leaving until I get twenty,' Wee Dave shouted back, deep dimples in evidence.

Three hours later, Wee Dave had successfully shot nineteen into the hoop before Dad called him to leave.

'Last one,' he pleaded.

'Okay, one more.'

'I must get this one, I must get my twenty,' he said, placing extra emphasis on this last shot. Left foot through the ball, it's in the air, in the air, Wee Dave knew it was close as soon as it left his foot, and as he watched in slow motion it dipped just below the hoop. Sprinting forward, he retrieved the ball.

'One more,' he shouted, rushing back to position.

'This is the last one, your mum has dinner ready.' Dad had worked his way towards the goal and as the next shot came hurtling towards him – a shot that was not even close – he caught it and started to walk towards the car. The only way Dad could get Wee Dave to leave.

Nineteen. Not twenty. Another failure… another waste of time?

The try-outs were fast approaching and Wee Dave had practised every day in the garden but he was bored. The area was tight and he could only practise skills and keepy-ups. Boring, lame, tedious. He needed to be let free, he wished for the big area of Lowerton but was only allowed there with Dad, who could only take him on weekends. And when Wee Dave wanted something, Wee Dave became Annoying Dave.

'Watch this,' Dad said, showing him a clip of players doing freestyle. Wee Dave was wide-eyed. Some of the things these players could do, wow! He set a target to try to complete two new skills per week. In the first week he taught himself to catch the ball on the back of his neck, the second skill was to perform a rainbow flick. Just like everything he had done before, this did not come easy, he was not a natural, so he practised hard each day. Completing the task alone was not enough, he had to do it ten times in a row to prove to himself that it was not was not a fluke.

By the time the weekend arrived, Wee Dave was so entranced by practising his new skills that he had forgotten about Lowerton, so it was with new-found enthusiasm that Dad was driving him over the Bridge.

Practice, practice, practice, practice. Non-stop practice. In the back garden, in Lowerton, back garden, Lowerton…

'They're here,' he shouted a few weeks later, jumping down from the sofa and sprinting to Mum who gave him a hug, wished him good luck and waved after the car.

In the Slymes' car there was not a peep, the two boys nervously looking out the window, Wee Dave bouncing his knees up and down, and Slyme picking his nose. There must have been something huge up there holding his finger in place.

With Slyme's father owning the Park, they found a parking space easily even though the traffic outside was at a standstill. Coming through the back door, Wee Dave felt like a celebrity, but he was quickly wiped off his feet as the mass of footballers sucked him in. Like a giant wave, they were tossed left, right and centre, Wee Dave trying his best to fight his way to the stairs, but also trying not to lose Slyme.

I need eyes on the back of my head, he thought, feeling someone trip him. He had just stayed on his feet but his number had gone. Oh no, the number. He searched on the floor, looking for his number. The number. Wee Dave could not be admitted without the number. Where is that number? An agonising pain came to his knees as he scurried across the ground, but there was no sign of it.

Well… career over before it has even started.

'Wee Dave. Oi, Wee Dave!' It was Slyme. 'Number 6 is you, right?'

Relief… elation. 'Yes, yes, thank you so much!'

Each player had been given a field number, a shirt number and a colour. Luckily the two boys were on the same field, Slyme having to wear red and the number 3, Wee Dave wearing black and the number 6. Wee Dave held that number firmly in his hand now, holding tight until they got to field 73. After a MouthMan scan they were on the field and he felt safe to stick the number on his shirt. Phew!

When the door slammed shut he looked up and saw ten coaches, nine of whom stood at the back wall, one approaching with a friendly smile.

'Dave! Junior! How are you boys?'

'Good,' they both said in unison.

'My name is Fergus,' he said reaching out his hand, which they duly shook. 'I am the coach of The Grange FC and I am really excited to see you play today, just relaaax, enjoy yourselves and play your normal game. No pressure.'

Pressure. Pressure of winning. Pressure of try-outs. Pressure of School. Pressure of exams. Pressure of being ten years old. Pressure. But here Wee Dave was told by this balding old man...

'No pressure.'

'Grab a ball and start doing keepy-ups, let's see how many you can get...'

And with that they joined the six other boys who were doing keepy-ups, which Wee Dave found boring so he started to practise his tricks instead.

'Looking good, young man,' Coach Fergus said as he walked around looking at each player. Not shouting at him for NOT doing keepy-ups, but giving encouragement for experimenting. How many coaches do this? Would you shout at a kid for not doing keepy-ups at the start of a session? For not doing what they are TOLD?

'Thanks, Coach,' Wee Dave replied, feeling on top of the world.

'Please David... call me Fergus,' he said with a smile.

Fergus continued prowling the field, praising every player for their skills and greeting newcomers with the same enthusiasm as before. How can he keep that enthusiasm for each player? Like a Broadway show... The best coaches must challenge themselves to perform in the same manner and with the same enthusiasm for each and every show, for each and every session, for each and every player.

Meanwhile, the other coaches were leaning against the back wall, some talking to each other, others having a coffee, one was even reading a newspaper. Which coach are you? Which coach would you like to play for? Which coach would you want your child to play for?

Once the players had arrived, the coach who was reading the newspaper folded it shut and set it on the side before calling them to attention, asking them to form a line in ascending order. *Like a regiment*, thought Wee Dave, wanting to put his hand to his forehead, stamp his foot and shout 'Sir, yes sir!'

'Number 3, BLACK!' Sergeant Newspaper shouted. 'Hurry up and get in line.'

The black Number 3 darted after his ball, which he had over-hit while doing keepy-ups, and got in line.

'Silly mistake to start with, eh?' Sergeant Newspaper sneered, making some of the other coaches snigger. There was something very familiar about him, similar to Stout, similar to Slyme's father, as fat as both with the same hairstyle, but a more round nose and black eyebrows which stuck out beyond his ears. The snide resemblance to a fat snake seemed to appear in all three.

Sergeant Newspaper coughed, waited for silence and addressed the group.

'Welcome to try-outs,' he bellowed, voice deep, posh, echoey. 'This could be your one and only chance to become a footballer, so starting from now it is important that you *LISTEN...*' he turned his head to the side and wiggled one ear. Patronising prick! '... and do everything you are told.

'When you hear your name I WANT you to walk forward and we will assign you to a field. Today we will start with four-v-fours and then move into a bigger match of eight-v-eight.'

Want, want, want. I want this, I want that. Why do coaches/teachers/politicians always WANT something?

Names were called and players were directed to a field and instructed to wait. Name after name after name, all a blur, nothing familiar, and then... Slyme Jr. Wee Dave tried to catch his eye as he walked towards the first field, but he was in the zone, too focussed to notice. Either that or he was bricking it.

Wee Dave was one of the last names called and was directed to a goal on the second field. He looked over his shoulder to try and catch a last glimpse of Slyme, but he got nothing. Why was he being ignored? The butterflies were becoming a nuisance in his stomach.

Butterflies? Where had they come from? The first drop of sweat had formed on his head and he could not stop shaking. He looked to his teammates – they were giants; he looked to the opposition – they were monsters. Wee Dave was frozen to the spot.

Meanwhile, the game got underway, passing him by with every blink, until the ball somehow ended at his feet. *What do I do? I don't know what to do!* Like an out-of-body experience, it felt like he was looking down on himself, thinking how stupid it was to be here, how dumb he was to think that he could ever become a footballer.

Panic-stricken, he took a big swing with his left leg, not wanting the ball to be anywhere near him, and as it floated through the air he realised he had made a massive mistake. It was not going towards the opponents' goal, it was not even going towards his own goal, it was heading straight for one of the coaches who was bringing a cup of coffee to his mouth and... BANG!

It hit the cup as if it was the bullseye and coffee went swooshing into the air, covering the coach from head to toe. He hopped from one foot to the other while shaking his hands in the air, which in normal circumstances Wee Dave would have found hilarious. However, he did not laugh, instead he shirked to the ground, hoping it would open and gobble him up. It did not.

The coaches stared at Wee Dave and with a shake of their heads they made a note.

'He's had a nightmare,' one said under his breath, although it was loud enough for Wee Dave to hear and he was heartbroken when a few of the other coaches giggled. Suddenly, Fergus marched straight for him and Wee Dave knew this was the end, but at least he would escape the Park. Far away and never to return.

'Don't worry Dave, just relaaax, enjoy yourself,' he said, hand on shoulder, guiding him to the side. He hunched to eye level, which was new for Wee Dave who always had to look up at people. 'Hey, keep going, you're doing great, okay?'

'I knocked the coffee all over him,' Wee Dave sobbed.

'So?'

'So I'm terrible, it wasn't even close to the goal.'

'And?'

'And I'm not going to play anymore, what's the point? Nobody will want me after that.'

'Young man, Mr Stout rates you very highly, says you're the best in School. You just need to calm down and play your game. Trust me, relaaax and enjoy yourself.'

Wee Dave was still annoyed with himself, but he felt better after hearing Stout's opinion. Fergus made him feel good, made him feel calm. He had a way with Wee Dave, spoke to him as if he was a normal person, as if he was interested. Wee Dave had become accustomed to adults belittling, ordering, demanding and commanding. Not Fergus.

Wee Dave, with his heart beating a little slower, smiled his dimples before returning to the field.

The play seemed much slower now that he was relaxed. None of the teams were in control as the ball bounced from shin to shin until it fell to Wee Dave. He expertly dribbled past two defenders before finishing into the bottom left corner. In the next play, he outmuscled one of the bigger lads who fell over in stages, played a one-two with a teammate and smashed one into the top corner with the outside of his left foot. It had been two minutes since Coffeegate, but how times had changed. The monsters had disappeared and he felt ten feet tall.

'Excellent,' he could hear Fergus shout from the side and caught a glimpse of his thumbs-up. The other coaches were starting to take vigorous notes, carefully eyeing each other over their iPads and no longer sniggering. *Shut them up*, thought Wee Dave.

A loud whistle blew for the end of the first game and Wee Dave had a screamer. Not only had he scored four goals, but by the end he was trying new tricks and with the last play of the game he had done a rainbow flick over a defender and volleyed it with all of his might, only for the ball to crash off the crossbar and go out of play. Wee Dave gasped and put his hands to his head, the other players' and coaches' jaws dropped collectively in disbelief.

'What a hit that was,' Sergeant Newspaper exclaimed, then... 'Get yourselves a quick drink and when you come back, Red teams switch fields, Black teams stay where you are.'

Freshly hydrated and with a spring in his step, Wee Dave ran to his goal and after doing a head count realised that the Red team had one extra player.

'Slyme! You're meant to be on the other field,' he whispered as loud as he dared. No response. 'SLYME,' he said more urgently, 'get your act together!'

Fergus walked across the field, guiding Slyme to the correct place and advising him all the way as Wee Dave stared after them, worried about his friend.

'Oi! Number 6, are you not going to play anymore?'

Wee Dave laughed to himself. *He must be really bad if the kids are shouting at him!* Then he snapped into action.

THEY'RE SHOUTING AT ME!

Once he got back to the field Wee Dave made an even better impression, bouncing around as if he was a man possessed. Time flies when we have fun and in the blink of an eye, the game was over.

The third and final game was eight-v-eight, he was told to play left midfield since he was the only left-footed player there.

What is left midfield? he thought, but knew better than to ask questions.

This game was significantly different from any other he had played, the sound and the noise from the shouting, screaming coaches made this 'game' into a bit of a circus. The coaches who were quietly going about their business in the first two matches had transformed into clowns for the third and final match. Why are they shouting? Why now? Maybe because it is eight-v-eight...

'Number 6, Number 6, get out wide.'

'Number 4, get back.'

'Number 7, go forward.'

'What are you doing on the left, Number 8, get back to your position.'

'Pass, pass, pass pass.'

'SHOOT!'

'Keep it on target!'

The last demand was aimed directly at Wee Dave, who had just fired one over the top of the bar. The rest of the noise was just that, noise. Wee Dave's ears perked up when he heard the call of 'Number 6,' but apart from that he tried to ignore the clowns, they were distracting him from the football. At one point he heard one joker shouting at Number 4, only for the Number 4 to stop and try to hear what was being yelled.

'Why have you stopped?' the joker screamed. 'Keep your eyes on the ball!'

Why do coaches shout like maniacs? Like clowns? Buffoons? They do not shout in maths class! How can we enjoy this? How can we learn? We cannot hear what coaches are saying when our focus is on the ball! The stupidity of these grown men shouting baffles the mind.

I suppose they're trying to help, I just wish I could understand.

At a break in play he strained to hear and squinted to see, and as he did so, he noticed that the only coach who was not barking was Fergus.

Chapter 7

Smile

At the end of the try-outs Sergeant Newspaper informed them that they would hear back within the next week, explaining that each coach in attendance was with a team from the Junior League – the youngest football league in the City – and that the lucky players may get more than one offer.

'I hope I get an offer from Fergus, the others coaches were maniacs,' Wee Dave said in the car, starting a rant about 'screaming morons' and wondering why they wouldn't 'shut the fudge up!'

'It's just like I said when you complained about Stout, they're yelling to help us,' Slyme replied.

'Exactly young man, and if you listen to what they say, you'll be in the League of the Sky in no time,' chimed in Slyme's father from the driver's seat.

'Well, I hope that I get an offer from Fergus,' retorted Wee Dave. 'At least he cared for us, the others didn't give two craps.'

The Slymes did not respond and the rest of the journey was spent in silence.

'Well boys,' Mum said once they arrived, 'did you have fun?'

Slyme shrunk low in his seat. Wee Dave on the other hand... The silence from the car made him feel like he was swimming underwater... forever. And when Mum asked this question it was like he resurfaced for breath, blurting about the 'maniacs', sucking in a huge breath of air before he started his sermon on Fergus.

Mum rolled her eyes to the sky, saying to Slyme's father, 'This one, once he gets something in his mind there's no stopping him. It wouldn't surprise me if he gave up football altogether if this Newspaper guy became his coach!'

Slyme sniggered at the comment, rapidly said goodbye and with a spin of the wheels, they were off. The screech of the tyres frightened Wee Dave and as he stared after the car he could see Slyme's father with one hand on the wheel, the other being used to viciously point his index finger back and forth, as his mouth snapped like Pac-Man.

I wonder why he is so angry... he thought, before turning to Mum and starting another long tantrum about Fergus and the clowns.

Exactly one week after the try-outs the letter box was full of post for Wee Dave, seemingly every coach had offered him a place. Wee Dave was only interested in one.

'Nope,' he said, after opening the fourth envelope and throwing it behind his shoulder.

'Nope.'

'Nope.'

'Nope.'

What if he didn't think I was good enough?

'Nope.'

'Yes!!! I'm with Fergus, I can't believe it. Although I knew I played well,' he finished rather smugly.

'Well done, son, we're both very proud of you,' Mum beamed, clapping her hands together and holding them in a prayer. 'Oh, good for you!'

'And we have a surprise for you,' Dad said, raising his eyebrows. 'Follow me.'

Wee Dave, heart skipping, followed Dad to the backyard where in front of him was the unmistakable shape of a bike covered in a sheet.

'No… way,' he breathed.

'Go on then… open it,' Dad encouraged.

Wee Dave grabbed the sheet with both hands, slowly unravelling what was underneath. It couldn't be a bike, his own bike. Surely not. He scrambled the sheet together in both arms and in front of him was a sparkling black bicycle.

'No… way,' he gaped. 'No way!'

'We know you studied a lot for your exams, and worked really hard to do well in the try-outs, we think you deserve something special,' Mum said, eyes glistening, teeth whiter and smile wider than Wee Dave had ever seen.

'This… is… definitely… the… best… day… ever,' Wee Dave stuttered and ran over to give them both a massive hug.

Wee Dave had never owned a bike, instead using the State's bikes to get to and fro. His hands were always black and sticky after using them, the wheels squeaked and in general, all of the bikes were rusting and falling apart. But the worst thing about the State bikes were the timers. Oh, the timer! How Wee Dave and citizens alike hated the timer. State bikes were only allowed to be used for one hour per day, each person using their phone to log in, in order to track them. But the timer on most of the bikes did not work and one day when Wee Dave was cycling home from School, there was a clunk of a thick metal bar as it locked between the spokes of the front wheel, bringing him to an almighty stop. He was on the bike for twenty minutes and he was speeding so fast – he needed to get home to finish his homework – that he flipped over the handlebars, performed a somersault and was lucky to land on his backpack. This happened on a regular basis in the streets of Middleton...

So the chance to own his own bike, go wherever he wanted to, for however long... Wow!

'You deserve what you can get,' Dad said, and with that, Wee Dave was gone.

An hour later he returned to Dad, who was leaning against the front door reading the day's copy of the *Bull Standard*. As he had been riding, a thought had come to him...

'Dad?' Wee Dave enquired, setting his bike down carefully. 'You know how I've got this bike?'

Dad rustled his paper and his eyes appeared over the top.

'Yes,' he answered.

'Well, I can go anywhere now, can't I? Like to School and the Park and stuff?'

'Of course, it's great isn't it?'

'Yeah, but...'

At this point Dad cut him off. He knew this was going somewhere and wanted to get to the point.

'Yeah but what?'

'Well, I was thinking, maybe I could cycle to Lowerton sometimes to practise my football...'

Dad went silent and returned his eyes to the paper. Wee Dave dropped his head in defeat, knowing better than to argue, and started for the front door.

'David,' Dad said in a serious tone, 'if I say yes, you must promise me that you will be back by 7 p.m. every night. No exceptions!'

'Of course, Dad,' Wee Dave answered. He then started to talk rapidly, as he always did in moments of excitement. 'Sure, why would I stay later than that, it gets dark and I can't play anymore. I wouldn't be able to see the ball or the goal, it would be silly.'

He took a deep breath and was about to continue but Dad stopped him.

'Just promise me,' he said.

'I promise Dad, I'll be home by 7 p.m. every night.'

Every day of the School holidays Wee Dave made the journey across the Bridge, and no matter what time he arrived, he always thought to himself, *I must be earlier, I need more time to practise.*

He asked Slyme to go to Lowerton but he wanted to stayed in the Park.

'Come on! Lowerton is so much better, it has bigger goals and the field is huge. And it's never used!' Wee Dave pleaded. 'It's great being outside as well, the fresh air definitely does me a world of good.'

No matter how much he pestered, Slyme never budged, although Wee Dave suspected that his father would not allow him. Slyme had become more interested in his new gadgets and toys.

I only need my football, Wee Dave thought, but he was in envy when Slyme brought his remote control helicopter.

'It's great that we're in the same team, isn't it?' Wee Dave asked, trying to move the conversation back to football.

'Yeah, I suppose.'

'I can't wait until next week, I've been trying these new tricks down at Lowerton and I think they'll come in really handy.'

'Probably.'

'What do you think we'll do first session?'

'Dunno.'

'I reckon it'll be loadsa matches, I hope it's matches, Fergus will let us play matches.'

'Yeah, maybe,' Slyme sighed, turning his attention to the skies, where his helicopter was chop-chop-chopping at the top of the Park.

On the day of the first training session, Wee Dave did not go to Lowerton.

'You don't want to be too tired for your first session, do you son?' Dad asked.

So Wee Dave did not know what to do with himself that day. Opening *The City Football Magazine*, he thumbed his way through, trying to find a decent story. *Crap, crap, crap, crap.* Flicking from front to back, back to front, he tossed it on the table and grabbed the TV remote. He searched through the 2000+ channels but found nothing. The family iPad was next, but all he could think about was Fergus, so he googled his name with no luck.

16:00. The Slymes were picking him up at 18:30.

'Mum, I'm bored. Do you think if I phone Slyme we could go to the Park earlier to practise?'

'Just relax, it's only a few more hours, why don't you watch some football videos? That will get you in the mood.'

'Yeah, good idea,' Wee Dave replied, returning to the iPad. He watched video after video after video. Then he watched a few more videos. He felt like he had been sitting there for about four hours, but when he looked at the clock…

16:25.

Wee Dave frowned and let out a groan of frustration. Two more hours!

He went to the backyard, had a scan and on the ground he noticed a tennis ball that the neighbours must have hit over the fence. Whether it was through pure irritation or boredom Wee Dave did not know, but he took a huge swing with his left peg, thundering the tennis ball against the fence, and with a thud it came hurtling back towards his face. A sharp step back, he let the ball land on his chest and followed this with three keepy-ups before losing control.

Two hours later, when the Slymes arrived, Wee Dave was still out the back and had a record of forty-seven keepy-ups with the tennis ball. He was a little downhearted walking to the car, having missed his aim of fifty.

Next time, he determined. Another waste of time…

In the car there was a strange atmosphere, a mix of nerves and excitement, pure silence as the two boys mulled over what was to come. Slyme had lost all interest in football but did not have the nerve to tell his father. All he wanted to do was play his PlayStation, he could control the level of difficulty so it was more fun. He knew that he had fallen behind Wee Dave and lost heart because of this.

His father had left the window down, which Slyme hated, the air cutting through him as he took one of his gloved hands away from his ear to wipe away the ice drip which had formed at the hook of his nose.

How I wish to be under my covers! he thought as he quickly covered his frozen ear, but his father had always wanted him to become a footballer, the only reason he had bought the Park, and Slyme could not let him down.

Slyme had been trained by his father from an early age, he had been dribbling around cones for as long as he could remember, but it was boring and he was doubting its effectiveness. He felt like he was getting worse but the one time he questioned his father, his PlayStation controller was banned.

'Dad, I'm getting better at dribbling around these cones,' he said on the way home from the Park one day, 'but as soon as I play against Wee Dave, he is much stronger and faster than me. I can't get the ball off him.'

'So you need to get faster around the cones, son,' came the reply.

'But…'

'But what?' his dad threatened.

'But how can I get stronger by dribbling around cones. They don't move! When I play against Wee Dave, he moves and I can't get past him.' Slyme gasped for air, more than a tear forming in his eyes.

'Well, you may get to this new team and try even harder!' his dad retorted. 'Or better still, I'll take that PlayStation off you!'

Sitting in the back of the car on the way to that first training session, Slyme felt like he was disappointing his father, not living up to his expectations.

This is my life, not his.

He has spent so much time and money on me becoming a footballer. I must succeed or I will be considered a failure in life.

That's not true! I can do anything I want, maybe one day I'll be Prime Minister.

Stop being stupid, you're journey is football. It's either that or the Lazies, maybe even Lowerton!

So what should I do, there's no way I'll be better than Wee Dave.

You cannot let Father down, he'll be so disappointed in you.

Not ideal thoughts for a young lad on his way to his first ever football practice, wishing that the car would never stop, hoping he was on a never-ending journey to nowhere. But there is no such thing, and as the car swung into the Park he sat inside for a moment too long, thinking how that was the quickest journey ever.

'That journey took forever!' Wee Dave exclaimed, jumping out of the car in extra-quick time. 'Come on, let's go! What's taking you so long?'

Oh shut up. Just shut up. I should just sit here forever. I wonder what would happen...

He did get out and tried to catch up with Wee Dave, thinking the only thing worse than attending this session would be to arrive alone. At least he was familiar with Wee Dave and maybe they would be on the same team.

'Hello boys, how are you?' Fergus beamed as they arrived together

'Great,' Wee Dave shouted.

'Alright,' Slyme mumbled, arriving just behind.

'Fantastic! Junior, you can join the Red team and Dave, you can join the Greens, the bibs are on the ground over there,' he said and pointed to two piles of red and green bibs. 'It's great to see you, go and have fun!'

'Straight into matches, I knew it!' Wee Dave said.

As more players arrived they were put into four teams and they played a three-v-three tournament, where they had to dribble through gates at either end to score a goal.

'The only rule is that you have to dribble, shots do not count. Please go out and show me your skills, don't worry about losing the ball or making mistakes, you're here to learn and have fun.' This was all that Fergus said throughout the tournament, except for the occasional 'Excellent', or 'Well done', or 'Good try', or 'Relax'.

The intensity was incredible, at first too fast for Slyme, but he played himself into the game. 'Hey, Slyme, you're doing amazing, keep it going,' he heard Fergus shout when the ball ran out of play. His heart was rapid, face red as a rose, and puffing his cheeks out, he let out a sigh of relief. The first praise he had ever received. Praise... What is praise? He didn't know, but it made him feel good, made him feel comfortable, confident. Strange...

Coaches, teachers, parents, bosses, people in charge, 'responsible people!' – they feel the need to criticise. Why not praise?

With his new-found confidence, Slyme won every one-on-one battle, even pushing Wee Dave off the ball with relative ease.

All thoughts of computer games and lying in bed had been lost, instead replaced with a new-found joy of playing football.

'Okay boys, brilliant tournament. I loved all of your dribbling skills, your speed with the ball was excellent, but most importantly when you lost the ball you tried your hardest to win it back. Now, let's *try* exactly the same in our final six-v-six, we will be using the goals but I'll be looking for your skills.'

The way that Fergus emphasised the word 'try' delighted Slyme and all he wanted to do was impress him, to work hard for him, to *try* for him. So that's what he did, he *tried* his skills, he worked hard in the big match, sometimes it worked, sometimes it did not, but Fergus would always repeat 'Good try', or 'No worries', and Slyme felt invincible.

They played three matches of six-v-six, Slyme did not for how long, but it was far too soon when it was called to a stop.

'Okay boys, very well done. I know I did not give many hints or tips just yet, but I really wanted to see how you played and I am extremely happy with every single one of you! Slyme, you were fantastic out there showing me lots of skills and Graham, I even saw you try a rainbow flick. Brilliant, absolutely brilliant,' he said and the two boys beamed. 'I love to see dribbling at your age, it shows that you can control the football and you have confidence in yourself, so we will continue to do that for the next few weeks. Everyone give me a high-five and you can go.'

With that he put his two hands in the air, but when Slyme reached to give him a high-five, he pulled it away. Others tried but with the same outcome. He then spun on his heels and took off, causing mass chaos as all of the boys chased him around the field. As he slowed the happiness was evident, smiles, smiles,

smiles. Smiles from the twelve boys. A smile from the coach. How often do you see that? Everyone loves a smile. Smile more. The boys had so much fun in the first session and could not wait for the next one.

After saying goodbye, Slyme and Wee Dave bounced back to the car.

'Is he not going to teach you anything?' his father asked as soon as they had buckled their seat belts.

The smile quickly vanished from Slyme's face.

'What do you mean?' asked Wee Dave. 'That's the most fun we have ever had.'

'FUN!!! You are training to be playing football, young man, not having fun.'

Slyme flashed a 'Please don't!' with his eyes. Wee Dave took the hint and not another word was spoken until Wee Dave left the car. Then... the dreaded car journey home.

Where is the smile?

Chapter 8

Coach Alan

'Ten more seconds, lads,' Coach Alan shouted. Dave's arms were shaking, his shoulders and chest in a world of pain as he tried to push himself back up, but fail, fail, fall. He gasped, knowing he had let the team down and they were in for another thirty seconds of push-ups.

Maybe he hasn't seen me, he thought when nothing happened. Then...

'NOT AGAIN DAVE, WE'LL BE HERE ALL NIGHT IF WE HAVE TO. ONE MORE MINUTE.'

Dave let out a sigh and started again. The rest of the team must hate him because of this extra punishment, but the agony, he wanted to cry out, he wanted to stop, quit, why is it so hard? Who knew professional football would be like this?

Each session was the same. First they ran three miles around Middleton, then it was a series of uphill sprints at the back of the Park, before sprinting the steps to the forty-ninth floor where they entered a field to perform a mixture of sit-ups and press-ups. At the end they played matches, but after the warm-up Wee Dave was so fatigued that he could barely stand.

Even the matches were boring, with Coach Alan stopping every two minutes to point and talk for five. Dave knew this was important, but his attention span drifted, thinking of the Glory Years, of Fergus, of cycling to Lowerton and practising his new…

'Okay, TIME! Well done lads, get a drink.' Dave was brought back to the present and having done what felt like a million push-ups, struggling to his feet was the easy part. Once there, his head was faint, his vision blurred and his body shaking. Stumbling across the field like a drunk, he headed straight for the 100-litre water tank.

Get there and I'll be okay, he thought.

Setting his eyes on the target, he wobbled closer until it was eventually towering over him. Leaning his arms on the tank and his head on his arms, he tried to catch his breath, but now that he had stopped moving it made him more dizzy.

It came from the bottom of his stomach, like a dragon had just been released from hell, green, gooey, sticky, lumpy sick all over the place.

After spitting the last bits on the ground and wiping the tears from his eyes he still did not have the energy to lift his head, he stared at the ground around him, a mess everywhere, all over the water tank as well. Oh dear!

Blink.

Blink.

Still hunched over but feeling much better, Dave took a deep breath. *Glad that's outta me.*

Blink.

Breath. The stench, oh dear!

Blink.

Shoes.

Sharp intake of breath.

Blink.

Shoes covered in slimy green bile. Eyes raising. Black trousers. What a state!

Blink.

Breath held… This is not a water tank…

Can't take another breath.

Belly. A huge belly, a belly like a planet. A belly with its own orbit.

Blink.

Eyes up.

Red face. Angry face. White spit frothing at the corners of Coach Alan's mouth, who was snarling like a dog. A very big dog.

'GET TO THE SIDE!' he pointed. Dave scurried like a mouse from a tiger and sat, watching the last ten minutes of training, the only ten minutes of football they played.

Another week on the bench, he thought.

Chapter 9

The Grange FC

The first few months of training with The Grange were much better than Wee Dave could ever have imagined. Fergus taught them how to dribble and trick defenders. One thing which really helped Wee Dave was when he spoke about changing speed, he had always been so fast that he could run past players with ease, but now that the standard was higher, he did not have the same success.

'Slow on approach, take little touches, change direction and a burst of speed to get away,' were ingrained in all of their heads after the first week. Fergus repeated these four points throughout the session and it was so easy to remember, but the most important thing for Wee Dave was that it was done in a one-on-one and was competitive from the start. To Slyme's relief, he was able to practise his skills around an actual person and not a cone. Imagine playing football against a person, eh?

The next week was the same but Fergus focussed on defending in a one-on-one. 'Fast, slow, side, low,' he would shout from the side after showing the team in stages. It was the way that he coached which really made an impression on Wee Dave, he was never angry and always used praise and positive examples. No belittling in this team.

'Look how FAST Wee Dave closes the space when defending,' he shouted when Wee Dave was asked to do a demonstration in front of everyone, making him feel like a king. He vowed to keep closing the space at that speed all of the time, eager to keep impressing Fergus.

Then he let them play, let them try to close the space at speed. He let them try. Let them play!

The next time he stopped to show a demo, he shouted, 'Can everyone see how Luke SLOOOOOWs on approach and stops at just over arm's length?' Luke threw his arm in front to give a visual aid of the distance he was from the defender. 'Let's see if we can all do that.'

If Luke can do that, I can definitely do better, Wee Dave thought.

Positive reinforcement, positive feedback. Praise. He made each and every player feel special, which made all of them fall in love with the game. He did not make them listen, he made them want to listen. There's a huge difference.

More time was given for matches as each week passed, but Fergus could still be heard at the side, reminding them of what they had been taught.

'Remember Austin, can we get SIDE on? Why do we do that?'

'So we can chase back,' Austin shouted as he did exactly that. He got the players thinking with questions rather than instructions, each player encouraged and given praise even if they were wrong. The players became more opinionated, willing to learn and eager to answer each question. But do coaches like questions? Do teachers like questions? Do politicians like questions? They bloody well should, and if they have no answer then guess what… they don't know their job. It's even worse if the answer is along the lines of 'Because I told you', or 'That's the way it's always been'.

These players are not PlayStation figures, they are people. Shouting random instructions such as 'PASS', 'SHOOT' and 'SPREAD OUT' does not magically make them do it. This is not coaching.

As the weeks progressed Fergus moved on from one-on-ones to two-v-twos to three-v-threes and so on. This allowed him to talk about the attacking and defensive side of the game with more people and it really helped the boys learn.

'Why do we make the field big?' he asked after doing three-v-threes.

'To create more space,' the team replied in unison. This had become the natural way to answer since Fergus had told them they were not in School, and did not need to raise their hands.

'And how does that help us?'

'It gives us more time.'

'To do what?'

There was a moment's silence until one of the boys, Duncan, answered. 'To make our decisions?'

'Brilliant Duncan, give me five.' After reaching across and slapping Duncan in the hand he continued his questions… 'What could these decisions be?'

'Maybe to pass?' Jake said.

'Or dribble,' chimed his brother Zach.

'Exactly boys, well done.'

'It could even be to shoot,' said Slyme, who had a new-found confidence during football.

'Fantastic. Another great session boys, give me five and I'll see you next week.' And with that he took off like a whippet, the flock of boys behind who were trying to catch him not getting close. Like a carrot on the end of a stick.

'Maybe next year, boys,' he shouted, still backing off and not letting anyone give him a high-five. As usual, every player left with a smile on their face.

And every night Wee Dave would join the Slymes for the car journey home, dreading it more and more each time.

'You boys are getting better but I just can't understand his methods. When the pros come to train they are so much more organised and they have lots of fitness, surely he should be making you do that!'

The boys waited in nervous anticipation, feet that could not yet reach the ground rocking back and forth, all eyes fixed to the floor. All except one, who had been so excited in recent weeks, who had practised so hard to become a better player and who was destined to go on and play to a great level ever since the day he hit his dad in the nose with what he thought was a pillow.

'Now boys, this is your first ever match, try to drown out the noise from the other side and don't worry about a thing. Let's practise all of the skills we have been doing in training, especially getting around the defenders. All will be grand, just try, try, try!' Fergus said with a smile. 'And remember, relaaax and enjoy!'

With that, the boys were on their feet, running to the field and Wee Dave looked over to the stands, trying to find his parents, but it was such a huge and boisterous crowd that it was impossible. He saw that Slyme's father was positioned at the front, smack-bang on the halfway line.

Probably to shout his lungs off at Slyme, Wee Dave thought, having become accustomed to this attitude from Slyme's father, who was beginning to shout at Slyme during training. Commands, demands, command, demand, do this, do that. Fergus quickly to put a stop to it, asking Slyme's father to be silent on the sidelines and let the kids make their own decisions. It was not an easy car journey after that particular incident.

Wee Dave remembered one time when the team had gathered at their usual lunch table in School, and after a mouthful of his chicken sandwich, Austin asked, 'Slyme, why does your father shout at you during training?'

Slyme went red and started to pick at his chips. 'To help me improve.'

'Sure, what good is that? You're not gonna get better with him shouting at you like a demon.'

'It's not his fault, is it? It's his father,' Wee Dave said, trying to come to the aid of his best friend.

'It's to help me improve,' mumbled Slyme, slouching lower and lower in his chair, staring at the plate of chips.

'He's a clown, mate,' Austin kept going.

'Yeah, a circus freak,' Luke joined in. 'PASS IT, SHOOT IT, KICK IT!'

'Is that what he's like when you're doing Maths? ADD, SUBTRACT, MULTIPLY!' Austin laughed. The team almost spat their food out with laughter.

'Or when you're reading... THE MAN WHO USES HIS FINGER,' Zach mimed with his index finger moving through an imaginary book on the table.

'Or when you're drinking,' said Luke and lifting his cup in his hand, he shouted over the laughter, 'LIFT THE CUP, KEEP IT STEADY, NO TILT OR IT WILL SPILL, BRING IT TO YOUR MOUTH AND SIP!' As he did this, Luke could not hold his laughter anymore and spat his drink all over Slyme. The team were on the floor after this, tears dropping from each of their eyes. Even Wee Dave had to laugh.

However, the tears in Slyme's eyes were not tears of laughter.

'Remember boys, relaaax and enjoy,' Fergus shouted from the side line, which brought Wee Dave back to the present. He looked at the other team and noticed how much bigger they were, but with Wee Dave being the smallest player in the School and having played against people bigger than him for his entire life, he had no worries. But looking at the rest of his teammates, you'd have been forgiven for thinking that they had just seen Godzilla.

'Come on boys, don't worry about their size, let's just try what Fergus has been coaching,' Wee Dave heard himself shout, trying to give the rest of the team confidence.

When the game got underway, the noise from the parents was incredible, all yelling their kids' names. The result of this was that every player in The Grange FC stopped on the spot and turned to look at the parents, thinking they had done something wrong. Meanwhile, the opposition ran through to score.

1–0.

'Eyes on the ball, boys, and remember let's drown out the noise, ignore the other side,' Fergus yelled, but it was barely audible.

It was hard to ignore the circus on the side, but the boys learned from the first mistake and kept their eyes on the game as play resumed. It was scrappy for the next ten minutes in which neither team played well, and each time there was a break in play, Fergus was heard offering encouragement and reminding the boys to try the little touches and skills they had been practising.

The next time Wee Dave got the ball he did just that, but took his touch too far ahead of him. The opposing defender took a huge swipe at the ball and as Wee Dave was slowly getting to his feet, he watched in horror as it came down from the clouds and landed in the back of the net. He hung his head in shame amidst cries from the parents:

'GET RID OF IT!'

'WHY DID HE NOT JUST KICK IT!?'

'PUT YOUR BOOT THROUGH IT!'

2–0.

'Hey, Wee Dave, great try,' Fergus called from the side once the parents had hushed. 'What can you do next time?'

Still asking questions, not commanding but making Wee Dave think.

'I need to keep it closer,' Wee Dave replied, happy that he had got some praise for trying, but still terrified that he had cost his team a goal. It was all his fault and the screaming clowns had made him aware of that.

'At least you *tried*! Remember, learn from your mistakes, but keep *trying*.' The emphasis that Fergus had when using any form of the word 'try' filled Wee Dave with confidence.

The next time Wee Dave got the ball, he did the same trick but this time kept the ball closer to him, he then glided past another two players before letting loose with his left foot.

1–2. Not many shouts of 'get rid of it' after that goal!

Another play with Slyme had resulted in the two of them dribbling and passing around the whole team, only for Slyme to round off a great goal. The two of them embraced, knowing that they had done something exceptional.

2–2. Half-time.

Fergus was beaming.

'Brilliant first half boys, excellent!' he said, making them feel proud. 'The first goal showed some great resilience from Wee Dave, he had lost the ball seconds before but learned from his mistake and still had the confidence to try. And it paid off! You should all learn from that.'

His smile was from ear to ear and Wee Dave returned it, heart hammering with the excitement of wanting to get back out for the second half.

'As for the second goal…' Fergus paused for a moment, looking around the group. He then looked over to the other side of the field and frowned. Slyme had not come in with the team at half-time, he had gone straight to his father.

'Um, yes, the second goal, fantastic from Wee Dave and Slyme, some wonderful skills.' He paused again, showing a slight hint of annoyance.

'So keep it up boys, you've shown me how good you are in training, so just go out there and do the same. And remember, relax and enjoy yourselves!'

Wee Dave was glad that he kept the talk short and sweet because all he wanted was to play. Returning to the field, they got a ball and started passing back and forth as they waited for the opposition. A pass went just beyond Wee Dave's foot and as he jogged to collect it, he caught a glance of the other team, sat in a circle on the ground, facing a remonstrating coach. The boys looked scared and daren't move. He lifted the ball and got away as quickly as he could, as if they were drug dealers and he needed to stay a safe distance from them, but he overheard the coach shouting, 'Look at them, they're all dwarves! How can you get beat by that lot?'

He was glad to get back to the safety of his own team, the smiles, the relaxed faces, kids who were evidently having fun, enjoying the game, like boys should. Well... everyone with the exception of Slyme of course, who had only this moment escaped from his father's rants. Some of the boys in the team had been nudging and looking in Slyme's general direction when they saw this.

'Come on lads, give him a break, he scored a wonder goal for us,' Wee Dave said, still trying to defend his mate. But he could not stop the bickering. Boys will be boys.

When the second half began, Wee Dave was so confident that if he got the ball he would score. After a long kick from the other team, one which he instantly plucked from the air, he played a one-two with Luke, touched to the left of the defender and rifled another shot into the top corner.

3–2. *Just like my shots in Lowerton*, he thought. Although School had started again, Wee Dave was able to cycle to Lowerton on weekends and practise his shooting.

As the game went on, Wee Dave found himself in defence a lot more. The opponents had put their two biggest players at striker and were kicking the ball high and long. But Wee Dave had always practised his aerial control and found it easy to get the ball down and play.

Entering the final fifteen minutes, with the game still at 3–2, all of the players were dead on their feet. All with the exception of one, who seemed to be growing stronger. Wee Dave thought of Lowerton and how his extra practice must have helped him as he sauntered through the opposition with ease, scoring another two and getting assists for goals from Slyme, Austin and Zach respectively.

8–2. Final score.

Throughout the second half, Wee Dave had learned to drown out the noise and concentrate on his own game, but the roaring from the parents and opposition coach had clearly affected the players from the other team. He was so glad that Fergus had warned them of this before the game, however, he noticed Slyme's performance dwindled as he continued to look towards his father. He was playing through fear and not joy…

Chapter 10

League of the Sky

Wee Dave did not want to take his hands out of his pockets, two pairs of gloves were not enough to keep the ice away from the bones of his fingers. His scarf smothered his face, making it hard to breathe, but without it, it would have been worse. A tear formed at the corner of his eye as he squinted at the back of the *Bull Standard*, trying to use the adults as a shield from the wind.

A PHENOMENAL START THAT IS BETTER THAN ANY IN THE HISTORY OF FOOTBALL.

He tried to read on but had to give up, crunching his eyes together and bringing a hand up to wipe the tear. But now his hand was freezing again so he quickly returned it to his pocket.

'Top of the league we are, 100% record and nineteen goals without reply,' he heard Slyme's father yell from behind the newspaper. 'Should be tough today though, Barnborough City are not far from here, somewhere over the hills I think. I heard they have this one winger who scores all of their goals, he's meant to be rapid.'

'Is that right?' answered Dad.

'But our right-back, Number 4, he'll have him in his back pocket. Best right-back in the League.'

'Awk, that's good, we're looking forward to it, aren't we David?'

'Yes Dad,' the obligatory response any young lad will give after his dad asks a question. But was he really looking forward to it? Watching football on TV had never interested Wee Dave, and he hated watching others play at the Park. But a match in the League of the Sky? To watch City play? To watch the best team in all of the land... could this peak his interest in football even further? After all, Slyme had been telling him for months about how good the atmosphere was, but never thought to invite him.

So this was his first League of the Sky match, a get-together that Fergus had organised for Grange FC's end of season party. And what a season it had been for Wee Dave, scoring in every game, but more importantly, learning in every game. He had become a more complete player, with Fergus teaching the team how to use little looks to scan the field and then make the correct decisions. He taught them how to play with their 'head up', he did not just shout 'Keep your head up', like some coaches do. There is a difference between teaching and telling...

Anyway... Mum had wrapped him in six layers which made him look like a sumo wrestler and he couldn't turn his head properly. He turned it as if he was in a cast, a broken neck and two broken shoulders, arms out like an airplane.

'You got those 1,000 credits with you?' Slyme's father asked after Wee Dave had rotated his wings to face forward. Because

Slyme was sitting with the team, his father now had an extra ticket and had invited Dad.

'Yeah, thanks for the ticket, we've never been before but the *Bull Standard* always reports about the atmosphere.'

'No problem at all. Do you not follow them on TV?'

'No, not really, we don't have the sports channels. We do watch the Buccaneers though, don't we son?'

'Yeah,' Wee Dave lied.

'Ah... right,' replied Slyme's father.

'We've had no luck lately though, this new manager has come in, big lad he is, and he has a bit of a reputation for being a disciplinarian. Apparently a lot of the players don't like his methods, he has them running loads but hopefully they'll come good sooner rather than later.'

'Yeah, hopefully,' Slyme's father sighed without any interest, and just as he did the bus pulled up.

Wee Dave and Slyme jumped on as fast as they could and found two seats beside each other. Slyme got his handheld PlayStation out straight away and got lost in that, some of the team followed behind and did the same. Wee Dave was looking at the tops of heads. Maybe people would grow eyes on the tops of their heads so they could see in front of them, the new evolved human.

Once everyone had climbed aboard and the bus had taken off, Wee Dave rested his head on the window, staring at the grey wall of Road Zero, train tracks above, but with it being so early there was no movement for miles. Nothing. A dead town. The mist, the grey, hazy air which always seemed to cover Middleton now, pure grey everywhere.

As the bus neared the Bridge to Upperton the greyness started to thin and the blue skies could be seen. Wee Dave loved staring at the sky, the clear blue beautiful skyline, lined with white clouds. Football clouds. There was a giant goalie glove, there were the posts, a boot, a football… His mind wandered. The blue skies… Why could he not see them in the winter? Why could he see them in Upperton but not Middleton? And definitely not in Lowerton… It was dark there, almost black… Ah, who cares, just focus on the clear skies for now…

'Has everyone got their passports ready?' Fergus asked, walking through the centre aisle.

After the passports had been collected a security guard from the bridge stepped onto the bus and walked to the back, scanning everything and everyone, tapping his fingers against his semi-automatic rifle as if playing a guitar. Once at the rear, he slowly turned around and walked to the front. As he did this another guard was shuffling through each passport, looking up, around, and then back down to the next passport.

'Reason for entering Upperton?' he asked while surveying the passports.

'We're heading to the City match.' After no reply, Fergus continued, 'For the football.'

'Okay. All looks in order here.' He gestured for the other guard to exit the bus. One more look around as he walked through the bus, all eyes set on him in nervous tension, but why? Why the tension? They had done nothing wrong, a group of eleven-year-olds going to a football match… Power, fear!

He climbed down the steps and waved for another guard to raise the barrier and let them through.

On entering Upperton, Wee Dave could feel the bus swerve to the left, to the right, to the left, to the right.

Wow! These roads are curved, he thought. Around the next bend another strange sensation hit Wee Dave. The bus seemed to accelerate downwards and his stomach was trying to jump out of his mouth.

Hills!

These roads were lined with castles, palaces with huge gardens at the front and back, gardens the size of football fields. Wee Dave's eyes widened as he noticed that some of the garden's actually had football posts in them, others had golf courses, swimming pools, fountains, horses were trotting around, sports cars on the fifty-yard driveways lined with trees, a helicopter, a runway, an airplane, statues, golden statues, gold everywhere.

'Wow,' he gasped, only this time out loud.

'I know, just off the bar,' Slyme said without looking up, evidently thinking that Wee Dave was commenting on his game.

Two and a half hours passed and Wee Dave still could not believe the beauty of what he was seeing, it was like he was in the middle of a dream. The mansions had been replaced by the bright green from the trees, the parks, the flowers. Yellow, red, purple, blue. It was so beautiful, so colourful. Natural. Wee Dave had only seen nature on TV.

The sun had risen, the skies were blue and although it was still a cold one, it was not quite as freezing as the morning. The shadow from the stadium loomed over them as they entered the almost deserted bus park, finding a space easily beside the entrance to the North Stand.

'You excited, boys?' Dad said as they jumped out.

'Yeah,' Wee Dave and Slyme replied in unison.

Wee Dave's jaw dropped in awe at the size of the stadium, it was bigger than anything he had ever seen before. It was circular like a football, and around the outside was a never-ending digital screen flashing highlights of the City players. As the team followed Fergus around the ground, Wee Dave noticed a statue that towered over everything, even higher than the stadium itself. It was an unmistakable tribute to the late, great Mr Smite.

'*Those who work hard will prosper*,' were the words engraved underneath.

Wee Dave was fed up of seeing these quotes everywhere but he would never think of voicing this opinion.

'This way, boys,' shouted Fergus from the front, raising a City flag on the end of a ten-foot pole with '*The Grange FC*' inscribed on it so that nobody could get lost. The boys filed through, showing their tickets to the MouthMen, and once they had entered the stadium, the temperature rose dramatically.

'Underfloor heating,' Slyme Sr said rather smugly. 'I doubt they have that at the Buccaneers?'

'Keep close, boys, we are B357,' Fergus yelled, trying to make his voice heard over the speakers.

On finding B357 the team began to ascend the steps, a mixture of a cool breeze from the outside air hitting their fronts and the underground heating hitting their backs. Wee Dave loved the feel of the cold air on his face, he always loved being outside and as he hit that last step and overlooked the pitch, overlooked the stadium, he felt like a bird that had just been set free.

Wow! he thought as he took in the pitch first, then the sheer size of the stadium. What a sight! He shuffled behind Slyme until they found their seats, still moving his head everywhere, taking it all in. Once they had settled, Slyme was straight on his phone and Wee Dave noticed that everyone else was doing the same. When I say everyone else…

'Where is everyone?' Wee Dave leaned and whispered in Slyme's ear.

'This is usually about it,' was Slyme's response.

'But there are so many empty seats!'

Slyme shrugged and looked back down to his phone.

'How many seats are here?' Wee Dave asked.

'250,000,' he replied. 'We have the biggest stadium in the world, "something to be proud of" my father says.'

'Sure, what's the use if there is nobody here?'

'Well, official attendance is always around the 200,000 mark.'

'200,000? Are you crazy? There's about 1,000 people here!' Wee Dave looked around and thought that even this was a gross exaggeration. It was harder to spot the people than it was to spot the empty seats, groups were scattered everywhere. In fact, the group making the most noise and seemingly having the most fun were all the way in the top corner of the stadium.

'Who are they?' Wee Dave pointed.

'That's where the away fans sit, they're usually very rowdy and cause trouble, Father says it's best to stay away from them, just in case, just in case…' he trailed off.

'Right… Can our dads not just come up here? There's loads of room.'

'At the moment there is, but what if someone comes?' answered Slyme. 'Father says we should stick to what the ticket says.' Again,

Wee Dave did not answer, but he was sure that other people would happily sit in different seats, considering there were so many of them.

'CLAPPERS, CLAPPERS, MAKE SURE YOU HAVE YOUR CLAPPERS!' A man was shouting, a bucket hanging from his neck.

'These are brilliant,' Slyme said, quickly digging his hand into his pocket, joy evident all over his face. Once he had bought it he showed Wee Dave how it was used by flicking his hand forwards and backwards, making the two wooden planks clap together. 'Only ten credits, too!'

'Here you go, young man,' the man said, handing one to Wee Dave.

'Oh no, I'm okay, I'll just use my friend's,' he said, putting two hands up to shoo him away.

'Excuse me?' the man demanded.

Slyme leant across and whispered in Wee Dave's ear that 'you have to buy one, it's rules and regulations'. Wee Dave frowned and unwillingly put his hand in his pocket, exchanged the ten credits for the clapper and folded his arms.

'Why did I have to buy this muck?' he asked Slyme, unfolding his arms and holding the clapper in the air.

'It creates an atmosphere, you'll see.'

'But ten credits!? Dad only gave me fifty, what if I need food or a drink?' Wee Dave demanded. He had crossed his arms again and was slowly sliding down the chair.

'Ah it's okay, you've enough for food, but not much else I suppose.' Slyme could feel the annoyance brimming in Wee Dave, so he tried to cheer him up by saying, 'I'm going to buy a new woolly hat, every game I buy a new hat or scarf to remember my day.'

After a few moments, more men with buckets hanging around their necks walked through the stadium selling food, drink and other memorabilia. Wee Dave saw a wallet which really caught his eye, but when he asked how much it was he scoffed.

'2,000 credits!? Are you serious?' He slammed it back into the bucket and again slumped even lower in his chair. 'I'll not be able to buy anything,' he huffed. Slyme fished the wallet out of the bucket, and along with a woolly hat and an iPad cover he exchanged 5,000 credits and put them all safely into his bag.

Next came the food and drink, both boys taking a menu and looking down.

SET MENU – 40 credits for 1 Main and 1 Side (includes a drink)
Main:
Pacific Ocean Black Cod Fillet
Buffalo Mozzarella, Poached Lobster
Corn Fed Free Range Chicken
Peppered Flat Iron Steak with Pommes Saladaise
Sides:
Sweet and Spicy Cucumber Slices, Smoky Mango Avocado Salsa, Garlic and Thyme Fondant Potatoes, Spicy Cajun Roasted Corn

'Um… I'll have the chicken and potatoes,' Wee Dave said after reading through the menu three times, unable to figure out what he was ordering.

'That's great, it'll be ready for the twenty-fifth minute,' the waiter said, and went to the next row to take more orders.

'The twenty-fifth minute?' Wee Dave asked.

'Ah, so the way it works is we chant and clap every so often, it flashes up on the banners, see?' Slyme pointed to the banners, which were currently flashing '*Shopping and Ordering Time*'.

'It's brilliant, the place goes wild,' Slyme continued. 'Anyway, from the twenty-fifth to the fortieth minute the food comes out so everyone has to be silent while we eat, manners and all that… But when it gets to the fortieth we crank up the noise for the final five minutes of the half. It really is fantastic, you will love it.'

The players started to jog out for a warm up and were waving up to the empty stands, cameras thrown into each face.

'Look now!' Slyme said and nudged Wee Dave in the shoulder, pointing at the banners which were flickering on and off with the word *CHEER*. The few people who were there made a noise, yelling at something, creating a sound more like that of a strangling cat in the distance. When *CHEER* was replaced by *CLAP* the cats were replaced by the sound of wood clapping, which sounded like a clock ticking. When the words disappeared there followed a murmur from the crowd as they started to discuss tactics and players.

Wee Dave, bored of the crowd by now, looked down to the players who were firing the ball back and forth at 100mph, effortlessly controlling it and pinging it to someone else.

'They're unbelievable, look how quickly they are moving the ball,' he said, turning to Slyme expecting a similar response, but to his dismay Slyme had buried his snout in his phone.

'Shush, the teams will be coming on soon, I want to see them before they're announced.'

There was a hush around the stadium as everyone did the same thing.

'Same starting eleven as last week,' someone shouted from below, evidently proud that he was the first to hear the news.

Moments later the teams were called over the tannoy, with a pause after each name to allow for a *CHEER* and a *CLAP*.

How fake is this? Wee Dave thought. After reading in the *Bull Standard* about the raucous atmosphere and hearing Slyme and his father talk the same nonsense, he could not have been more disappointed. *This isn't atmosphere, this is not delight and joy, this is doing what you're told!*

As the game got underway, Wee Dave could not believe how quickly they were moving the ball, it was touch pass, touch pass, touch pass, like the ball was a grenade and nobody wanted to hold it, but the speed and precision with which it was played. Wow!

He began to notice patterns in the game.

'That right-back, is he any good?' Wee Dave asked.

'Best in the business,' replied Slyme.

'He looks slow to me, that left-winger seems very tricky. And rapid!'

'Ah, don't worry, our Number 4 is quality.'

It was clear to Wee Dave that the away team's play was all down the right-hand side, leaving the tricky left-winger in acres of space. Ten minutes into the game and with about 90% of the play down one side, the ball was quickly switched to the left-winger who had all the time in the world – he could have made and served a pot of coffee to a roomful of toddlers – and before there was a defender near him he rifled a shot into the top corner. 0–1.

'I saw that coming a mile off,' Wee Dave chimed, proud of himself.

What was baffling was that nobody else seemed to notice, not even the coach, because five minutes later the exact same play unfolded, only this time the Number 4 was in a better position but the left-winger got past as if he wasn't there, then laid it back for the striker. 0–2.

'Is he going to change this? Or is he going to pick his nose and do nothing?' Wee Dave said, still annoyed that no one else had spotted the obvious. 'They're playing down one side, leaving the other side totally open for their fastest and trickiest player!'

Wee Dave was frustrated at the lack of eyesight from those around, but his level of frustration rose to a complete high when the food came out in the twenty-fifth minute.

'What the hell is this?' he demanded from Slyme. 'This can't be all of it!'

In front of him was a plastic plate the size of the Grand Canyon, and the food in the centre the size of a solitary pea. Three spoonfuls later, when he had finished the food and his stomach was still rumbling, he threw the plate into the air as City had gone 3–0 down with another identical play leading up to the goal.

'This is embarrassing!'

'They're not playing great, but we'll come back to win, we always do,' Slyme informed him.

'I'll believe it when I see it,' Wee Dave said and slumped into his chair.

The second half was boring, as the away team kept possession, even the 'incredible' atmosphere did not help City get the ball and they ended up losing 4–0.

'Last time I'll go and watch that crap,' Wee Dave said. 'That was ridiculous.'

'Keep your voice down please, David,' Fergus pleaded. 'We don't want to offend any of the loyal supporters now, do we?'

Best team in the world, my arse, Wee Dave thought to himself.

On the drive through Upperton the sun had completely set, it was pitch black except for the glow of phones and games consoles in the bus. Wee Dave gazed out the window, daydreaming, listening to the radio chattering about the match. His eyes became heavy after such a long day, his blinks became longer as darkness ensued, the sound of the radio fading, fading... fading, and just as Wee Dave nodded off he heard about another fantastic victory for City in front of a sold-out stadium who made a boisterous atmosphere.

Chapter 11

The Bull Standard

BUCCANEERS 1–0 DOLPHINS: ANOTHER BORING WIN
FOR THE CHAMPIONS

IN another drab 1–0 win for the Buccaneers, fans and pundits
alike did not have much to get excited about. Although they are
top of the league, COACH Alan is under much pressure from the
board since they have not reached the heights of last season. He
had this to say after much questioning about recent performances

'Listen, we're still top of the League and we're not giving up
many points. What do you want me to say?'

However, when asked about the performance of NEW
SIGNING Dave BLANCH he was quick to point out that things
can only get better for the young man.

'He's been here for half a season now and there is some small
improvement. The way the boy started we all thought he was a
lost cause, but we're beginning to see signs of progress.'

These comments have been taken with a pinch of salt by most experts.

'The Wee Man has been a disaster from his debut, he's useless with the ball and even worse without it!' one TV pundit said.

'He'll never make it to the League of the Sky. No commitment, no passion and no confidence,' former City player, Gary Burns stated.

COACH Alan claimed through obvious disappointment that today he was meant to be playing 'at the top of a diamond', and the fact that his heat map showed that 'all of his touches were in and around the centre circle' bugged him.

'Something we'll have to work on in training.'

Once tipped as a 'future League of the Sky superstar', it is hard to see where Dave BLANCH, 15, will go from here. With the Buccaneers still fighting on all three fronts and the pressure to emulate what they did last season, COACH Alan will find it hard to risk him in the big matches, although he has been heard to say that 'the boy's trying too hard to impress'.

Most experts are convinced that this lazy, unworthy and useless coward is a liability and will not feature much for the rest of the season. Others go on to say that his career is over already!

Only time will tell if this is the case, or if things will get better for the Wee Man.

Chapter 12

Welcome to Paradise

Two years had passed and Wee Dave still loved playing for The Grange, improving each week with the guidance of Fergus. He practised at Lowerton every weekend, coming up with new games himself, and loved the freedom of this, each week setting his alarm earlier so that he ended up cycling to Lowerton in morning darkness.

Mum could see his excitement build as the weekend approached and even made him a packed lunch so that he would not get hungry. Usually, Wee Dave would not let himself eat until he had finished a challenge – such as hitting the crossbar fifty times – sometimes he became so engrossed that his sandwiches were eaten on the cycle home.

He was now using his right foot more, as recommended by Fergus, and he could feel it getting stronger. One day he invented a challenge for himself where he had to do one keepy-up with the right foot, one with the left, two with the right, two with the left, three with the right, three with the left and so on and so on until the ball dropped. As usual, this proved extremely difficult at first but the more he practised, the higher he was able to get.

Right, I'm not leaving until I get ten.

This proved to be a hell of a lot harder than he first thought, but Wee Dave, persistent as always, kept trying until dark.

Last go, he thought after each failure.

I'll have to leave after this one.

Right, two more goes, if I don't get it, I'm gone.

Last one.

One more.

So close, I'll get it next time.

It was pitch black by now and he could barely see the ball so he trudged to his bag, another failed challenge, another waste of a day, and just as he swung his leg over his bike…

'You! I haven't seen you in ages, mate! What's the craic?'

Wee Dave's heart skipped a beat. Week after week, month after month and year after year, Wee Dave had been coming to Lowerton and had forgotten the reason he came here in the first place – after all, Jamie did say he practised here every day. He spun on his heels, and at first glance he could tell that Jamie was a shadow of when they had last seen each other, now much paler and skinnier, but the smile and joy were still apparent.

'Hey, I've been here every week for two years… and every day of the School holidays! I haven't seen you once, I thought you said you practised here every day!' Wee Dave said, clearly very agitated.

'Aye, I do.'

'What do you mean? I've just told you, I come here eve—'

'Yeah, I heard what you said, I come every night after work and I ain't seen you once, so right back at ye!' The smile had not left Jamie's face, as one foot began rolling the ball from side to side.

'But…' Wee Dave stammered. 'It's dark.'

'So waaa?'

'So… how can you see the ball?'

'Dunno, s'pose you get used ta it.'

Wee Dave stared in shock, not knowing what to say, so Jamie continued.

'Anyway, the rest of the lads'll be down soon so you should hang around and play.'

'You play matches?' said Wee Dave, jaw dropping to the floor.

'Of course lad, that's what it's all about, every night after work we're here, all night.'

'What do you mean after work? What about School?'

'Sure I told ye last time,' Jamie fired back, 'we don't get no edication in Lowerton.'

'So what do you do then?'

'I'm a cleaner but I also do foties for some bloke fer the newspapers. Nat the greatest, but it gets me and me Granda through the week.'

Wee Dave studied Jamie, black bags sagging under the eyes, the paleness of the skin blending into the white shirt – well, it used to be white, it was filthy now, more brown than white. Three-quarter-length trousers had slashes down the sides of both legs and big toes came out of holes in both shoes.

Feeling uncomfortable, Jamie flicked said shoes off and started to dribble with the ball.

'Mon, bet you can't get the ball off me. You'd have to be better than last time when I hammered ye!' Jamie laughed. 'Although I'm sure you don't 'member that with all thon other muck you bais from Middleton play, PlayStations and all that garbage, Granda says it's ruining the lives of everyone now, all this new treknolorky.'

'Nah, PlayStations are not for me mate, I just love playing football,' Wee Dave responded.

'Mon then,' Jamie said and bounced away, Wee Dave hot on his tail.

The two kids played like this until the next person arrived, short introductions were made until the three of them were chasing after the ball. When the next player came, Jamie grabbed him by the shoulder and said, 'You two v. us two.'

As more and more people arrived they were separated into teams, until eventually there were twenty-five players on the full field.

'Usually it's twelve-v-twelve,' Jamie remarked, 'But you're here today, makes it unfair, dunnit?'

'Sure you can sit out and watch, you're the worst player,' Wee Dave laughed. 'There's no way I'm stepping out, this is brilliant.'

And so they played for the next two hours, it was the hardest but the most enjoyable game that Wee Dave had ever been involved in. He scored, he dribbled, he passed, he tackled, he had fun! He played football!

Fun, the most important quality for any young player to improve. Fun.

His heart sank when he heard a loud voice from the top of the field.

'David, let's go!'

In all of his excitement, he had lost track of time.

'Please Fergus, come and watch us, he'll definitely be good enough to get in any team,' Wee Dave pleaded. He had been pestering Fergus for the last three months to come to Lowerton to see Jamie play.

His third and final season with The Grange was coming to an end, and what a successful season it had been, his best to date, and he couldn't help but feel the extra matches he had been playing in Lowerton for the last ten months had made him the player he was in these weeks approaching the next try-outs, for the Amateur Leagues.

'The boy's a natural,' his uncle said, which left Wee Dave frustrated. He had worked so hard to improve his ability that when he heard talk like this, it made him feel like his effort was underappreciated.

The main thing that drove him on was the competition against Jamie, the two of them inseparable after their chance meeting. After many arguments and much persuasion, Wee Dave was allowed to go to Lowerton on two of the nights he did not train with The Grange, and at weekends, but the two conditions were that his homework was finished and Dad was with him when it was dark. This seemed very reasonable to Wee Dave, who began doing his homework during lunchbreaks in School to allow him to spend more time with his best mate, Jamie.

Which brings us to Wee Dave asking Fergus about going to Lowerton to watch them play...

'Okay, okay,' Fergus replied. 'I'll come and watch on Saturday. It's that time of year when I need to scout for next season anyway.'

That Saturday, Fergus entered Lowerton, hobbled down the tree-lined pathway towards the field and took a deep breath of the black air. He had lived in Middleton for the past fifty years and had seen first-hand the massive rise in pollution.

Mr Smite had been an environmental activist during his reign and had tried his best to improve the air quality. He had introduced rented bicycles, made it mandatory for all cars to be electric and abolished all of the plastic in the City. However, Mr Smite, being from a well-to-do family who loved their food, did not think there was any need to prohibit meat, which happened to be one of the main causes of pollution worldwide. On the contrary, Mr Smite had ensured that there were three 100-storey factory farms, where millions of animals were caged, injected, fattened, annihilated and ultimately produced as meat. The smoke from these factories produced a layer of grey across the skies of Middleton, but Mr Smite had found a solution. The Fan. The Fan was a huge wind generator which blew most of the polluted air into Lowerton.

The Fan, which blew the black air down Fergus's lungs as he crouched to take a seat against a tree, knees creaking as he did so. He set his walking stick beside him, took his handkerchief out to wipe away the sweat on his brow and looked down at the field. He made sure to stay at a good distance, staying anonymous as he watched the game he loved.

Young lads playing football, you don't see that anymore with all the NO BALL GAMES signs and busy roads, he thought, looking to the black fog across the sky and thinking how dark it was here. He looked at his watch which told him it was only 12:30.

He hated the game that football had become. When Fergus was a kid he loved playing football on the streets, playing match after match against anyone who wanted to play. Something similar to what was happening in front of his eyes. But the game had changed over the years, with coaches overcomplicating the game. With the signs and busy roads stopping kids from playing street football, Fergus believed that coaches should have been able to adapt, creating an environment of fun where the players would learn and the coaches would guide.

On the contrary, coaches were either incapable of doing this or put a lot of equipment on the ground to make themselves look busy. What was this equipment for? Who was it for? Was it to make the coach think he was doing something? Was it for the parents? Was it for the TV? It was for anyone but the children, who were there to play football. The coach would then facilitate some form of drill or drills and have very little time for a match at the end. Some had no sense of time management, and focussing so much on the drill allowed NO time for a match. Others used the threat of no match as a punishment.

Fergus was annoyed that the game of football had been stolen from the people who mattered the most: the kids, the players.

In the days before Mr Smite and the League of the Sky, it was much worse. Children were being signed by professional clubs at the ages of three and four, kids who could barely walk. When Mr Smite and Mr Sky took over, they made progressive changes to the football system, no longer were the days of players being signed at a single-digit age, so in theory this was a good move.

However, this allowed the agent system to take shape. Before, the professional clubs and coaches did not want to miss out on a superstar – now it was the agents who were afraid of missing out.

As soon as a young kid with any potential came along, there was a long line of agents vying for his signature. All with the intention of selling them on to a professional team when they became fifteen years old. Even after this, the agent still owned the player, and if a team from the League of the Sky came calling, more often than not they were sold at the correct price.

Child trafficking. Disgusting, but somehow legal.

And what about the 99.9% of players who do not make it? They were dropped by the agents as if they were throwing away an empty chocolate wrapper. The CULLED!

This was the reason Fergus had taken a big step down in football. He tried to make it different, but kids and parents alike were made promises, given too much money too young, and no matter how many times Fergus warned the families, the bright lights and dollar signs of Paradise were too hard for them to resist. Fergus could not blame the families: it was the system, it was the agents. In no other walk of life could people make money on children, only in football.

That's not to mention the pills kids were taking from an early age in order to become the perfect build, the physical specimen of a top football player. He had recently read an article in the *Bull Standard* outlining the next experiment, forcing certain men and women into relationships, so that the best genes could be passed on to the next generation. Kids who were pressured to become a footballer, a tennis player, a mathematician, a doctor, etc., etc., before they were even born. What world is this we live in? The race to the bottom taking on new levels!

And as he watched Wee Dave and the very talented Jamie, he thought of what lay ahead in their futures. They both certainly had the skill, more importantly they had the passion and the will to improve. He would guide them as best as he could, he would always be there to advise them, a promise he had made to so many players before, a promise which had fallen on deaf ears. He was a man of the past, a forgotten coach, the one who waited by his phone ready to offer advice, a wise old man who preached youth, encouraged fun, who thought of the kids as people and not commodities, a man who did not belong or benefit from this day and age.

What's the point? he thought to himself with a sigh. And then…

'Fergus, I'm so glad you came,' Wee Dave yelled, waving from below. 'Have you been here long? What about that back flick from Jamie? You know, the one that hit the bar? Did you see?'

Fergus looked at that smile with loving eyes, that smile that promised so much hope, and it brought him back to his senses. *That smile is my Paradise*, he thought, and vowed that even if he changed the life of one person, he would be proud of himself.

'Of course I saw, it was incredible,' he replied.

'You think me and Slyme are good together, wait until you see me and Jamie next season,' Wee Dave said with a confident smile. 'Of course that's if…' he tailed off.

'Don't worry young man,' Fergus said, 'Jamie will be highly recommended. And I have no doubt that if you end up in the same team, you will torture opposing teams next season.'

The following season Wee Dave and Jamie did make the same team, and although Wee Dave did not like his new Coach as much as Fergus, the two of them did exactly what had been predicted, they tortured the opposition. Wee Dave would never forget Fergus and all that he had done for him, and Fergus was delighted that he still phoned him for advice.

'Fergus, when I'm in possession of the ball do you think I should still try my tricks, or should I try to keep possession?' Wee Dave asked him one day, after a session in which the new Coach was trying to encourage the team to pass, pass and pass. He didn't even say 'hello' or introduce himself, Wee Dave was always straight to the point.

'It depends on the situation of the game. Sometimes you should try to dribble forward and if you cannot do that, then it is time to think about starting the move again,' Fergus replied.

'Okay, thanks. Did I tell you about me and Jamie from the match on Saturday?'

'Yes, you phoned me on Saturday night, remember?' Fergus laughed, having become accustomed to these calls.

'Oh yeah... So on Saturday, will you come to watch us? This weekend we had planned to go and watch The Buccaneers play after.'

'I don't think so. I'm an old man now, I can't get about like I used to.'

'Please Fergus, Dad won't let me go to without an adult, and I've never been before, Jamie says the atmosphere is amazing.'

It had been a long time since Fergus had been to a Buccaneer Falls game, but if it was anything like it was when he was young, he knew the boy would love it. After a few more minutes of pestering from Wee Dave, he gave in and agreed to take them.

It had been nearly a year since Fergus had seen them play in Lowerton, and having reached the sixty-seventh floor of the Park, the floor for the League of the Young, he entered the spectator area and sat in the back row, away from the usual hustle and bustle, away from the noise of the parents. He could not believe the transformation in young Jamie. Although still slightly skinny, Jamie had beefed up a wee bit, looking more like a normal kid, unlike the lump of bones that usually comes from Lowerton.

Teams in the League of the Young provided players' food, and this was one of the main reasons Fergus continued to scout in Lowerton. He was the only person who did so, knowing that these people had to work hard to survive from a very young age, and he held the belief that the best footballers worked hard at their game. Kids from Lowerton only had football, they did not have the distractions of PlayStations or other games consoles. So, putting all of this together, Fergus had a great record of scouting players and helping them through the ranks.

Alongside Jamie and Wee Dave was a much chubbier Slyme, his face and demeanour becoming more and more like his father's. He got annoyed when he did not get the ball, threw his toys out of the pram when he lost possession and never thought to chase back and help his team defend.

After the final whistle, a game which finished 3–0 with Wee Dave and Jamie getting on the scoresheet – but more importantly to Fergus, enjoying their football and playing some exciting stuff – the two of them came hurtling over the hoardings and ran to the back of the stands where Fergus was sitting.

'Thanks for coming,' they said in unison.

'My pleasure, you were great. Shall we get some chips?'

'Yeah, let's go,' and with that they were in deep discussion about the game they had just played, Wee Dave leading the way, excitedly talking about the team's moves and not the wonderful individual performance he had put in.

This boy is definitely beyond his years, thought Fergus.

They ate their food in the car, and as they drove over the Bridge to Lowerton the weather took a vicious turn. Wee Dave and Jamie did not even notice through all of the excitement as talk began of the Buccaneers, Wee Dave asking all of the questions of the day, with Jamie only too pleased to answer. Fergus was busy concentrating on his driving, the windscreen wipers not making the slightest effect to the hammering rain.

'I hope the game will go ahead,' he shouted, but they did not seem to hear him.

After sitting in traffic for what seemed like forever, they found a parking space not too far from the stadium and got out to walk. As they got out of the car the wind hit them, blowing Wee Dave's hat straight off his head. Luckily, a man behind caught it in mid-air and saved it from any puddles.

'Here you go young man,' he said with a smile. 'Mon Buccaneers!!'

'MON Buccaneers!' Jamie shouted back to him. It was like a war cry which awoke the mob of supporters around them and they all started shouting 'MON Buccaneers!' Wee Dave shoved his hat back on his head and they joined the herd who were now chanting a song, one which Jamie was well rehearsed in and was singing as loud as possible.

'You're crazy,' Wee Dave shouted, battling his way through the storm and holding onto his hat for dear life.

'What d'ya mean?' Jamie replied.

'Singing like that, what is this, choir practice?'

'These are Buccaneer songs, they are a strong tradition of this club, something that brings Lowerton folk much closer together. Half of Lowerton will be here tonight, just you wait and see,' Jamie tailed off.

Wee Dave did not argue, he was being ferried along in the middle of a flock of supporters who were heading straight to the stadium. Elbows were hitting his head, toes were kicking heels, stale sweat was in the air, but nobody seemed to mind. On the contrary, everyone was so excited to get into the stadium and start singing songs.

After an hour of queuing for tickets, and Jamie teaching Wee Dave the words to some of the songs, they entered the stadium and it felt to Wee Dave like they had just walked onto cloud nine. He tried to take everything in – the pitch, the fans, the players warming up – but he didn't have time as they were ushered to their seats. The wind and rain was swirling, throwing rubbish into the air, an empty bag of crisps seemingly dancing along with the sound of music. Oh the noise. The NOISE!! Wee Dave had never experienced noise like this.

'How many fans do you think are here?' He shouted to Jamie who, two feet away, did not hear a thing. After poking his shoulder he asked the question again. Jamie responded by pointing to the right ear, shrugging shoulders and mouthing that 'I can't hear a thing'. Wee Dave, cupping his hand around Jamie's ear this time, screamed the question again.

'I dunno, probably around 100,000,' Jamie shouted, although Wee Dave struggled to hear.

He didn't know where to look; the bouncing fans, the dancing rubbish, the big man just below with the drum, a skinhead with a microphone leading the chants, it was too much to take in. Until a beast of a man sat in front of them. All he could see now was a brown leather jacket.

What will I do now? he thought, turning to Jamie and sighing his disbelief. *How unlucky am I?*

A shaking Jamie used Wee Dave's shoulder to climb onto the seat, and then gave Wee Dave a hand up so they could see the whole world again.

'Careful guys,' Fergus shouted but his voice was drowned out.

This is unbelievable, Wee Dave thought. Although he could not see the field anymore because of the waving flags and banners, the noise was breathtaking, the brown and red colours of the flags, shirts, hats and scarves showing the support of their team. It was art, like a beautiful autumn painting. There was no need for banners to tell the supporters when to cheer and clap, it was a wall of sound with fans bouncing to the beat.

The noise died a little as the game got underway, and Wee Dave stood on tiptoes to see. At one point he leant forward too much and fell onto the shoulders of the man in front.

'Stay there if it's a better view,' was his response, which took Wee Dave by surprise, he thought the man would have told him off.

'Are you sure that's okay?' he blurted.

'Of course,' he said jovially, 'I was in your position many times when I was a nipper.'

So Wee Dave found himself leaning on the back of a stranger, feeling more and more comfortable than he ever had in his life, feeling like he belonged somewhere other than a football field. However, nothing could prepare him for what happened when the ball hit the back of the net. Every fan jumped to their feet screaming with joy, the man in front turned around and gave Wee Dave a huge bear hug, lifting him high into the air as the rest of the crowd cried in unison, 'MON Buccaneers!'

After Wee Dave had been set back down, he found himself jumping along with the crowd to another chant. He could feel his legs wobble underneath him and as he steadied himself he was sure that he could feel the stadium rocking under his feet, but no one cared, they were here to have a good time and support their team, they were lost in the moment. Nobody was on their phone, food was not brought out at a certain time, this was real atmosphere.

And as they filed out of the stadium after the match, he tried to sing along with the rest of the fans but his throat had gone, his legs were aching and the gale was almost blowing him over. Even after a 2–1 defeat, these fans were still singing and dancing along the streets.

Fully drenched when they got to the car, Fergus gave them a towel to wipe themselves dry. But Wee Dave's clothes were damp as hell, they clung to him making him shiver, and Fergus got a blanket from the boot of his car and wrapped the two children in it, putting the heat on as soon as he settled into the driver's seat.

'Did you enjoy, guys?' he asked, smiling as he put the car into drive.

'Unreal, pity we couldn't get a win though,' Jamie replied.

'Best day ever, Fergus,' Wee Dave answered, still shivering but two dimples forming at his cheeks, cheeks in pain as he had never smiled for so long in his life.

He could not help but reflect on the last year of his life. A year spent with his best friend, Jamie. A year where his football had hit another level. But the icing on the cake was coming to see the Buccaneers with Jamie and Fergus. He loved Fergus. He loved Jamie. He loved football. He loved the Buccaneers.

Wee Dave, welcome to Paradise!

Chapter 13

Almighty Smite

MORE VIOLENCE IN LOWERTON AS THE LOCAL
FOOTBALL TEAM LOSES YET AGAIN
FOOTBALL THUGS ON NON-STOP DRINKING BINGE
WATCH OUT! HOOLIGANS!
TRIBAL WARFARE
A DISGRACE TO SOCIETY
THEY SEEM TO RELISH AND ENJOY THE VIOLENCE!

These were just some of the headlines on the back of the *Bull Standard* after each Buccaneers game. Under the last one was a photo of a group of men lining the streets with their arms in the air, looking like they were ready to attack, like a scene from *Braveheart*. Front and centre was a fat man with no shirt, belly covered in tattoos and a speaker held up to his mouth. Behind him more men with flags, scarves, hats and shirts, all brown and red, standing in unison with their arms high in the air, mouths open and yelling their war cry. The picture was filled with joy/hatred, with happy/angry faces in the middle of a chant/fight. Whichever way you look at it... But there, in the very bottom right-hand corner of the picture, were Wee Dave and Jamie, having the time of their lives.

Wee Dave folded the paper and threw it on the table before leaving the house and grabbing his bike. The last few months had been Paradise. He had continued playing football at a high standard and had become a regular at Buccaneers matches with his two best friends, Fergus and Jamie. The next two days would define everything, the League of the Youth had come to its final days with agents, scouts and coaches from the Amateur Leagues in attendance.

Twelve- to eighteen-year-olds played in the Amateur Leagues, in order to prepare them for the Professional League. Of course, there were some exceptions to this rule who had made it to the Professional League when they were only sixteen. In fact, McCrick, City's best player, was in the Professional League when he was fifteen and by the time he was seventeen was in the League of the Sky. Thousands of agents and coaches ended up in a serious fight for his signature, which ended up as a dust cloud with fists and shoes coming out of it. A cartoon brawl.

'Big day mate,' Jamie said, who was waiting for Wee Dave at the Bridge.

'Yeah, you nervous?' Wee Dave replied.

'Nah, nat really. I'll give it me best, s'all we can do.'

They took off, the breeze beating against Wee Dave's hair as they flew past the endless traffic on the way to 10/10. After locking their bikes in the designated area, Jamie shouted, 'Catch me if you can!' and was off like lightning, giggling away with Wee Dave hot on the heels. Little legs were going like the hammers until... STOP!

A MouthMan positioned at the entrance stopped them for a scan.

'These lads are useless ya know, don't have a clue what we're saying, do ye?' laughed Jamie, opening his passport for the MouthMan to scan. 'Nothing but morons.'

Wee Dave smiled, and joining in said, 'Yeah, you don't even have eyes. Machines. Nothing but machines. What a worthless existence in this world.'

'HELLOOOO!' Jamie yelled, frantically waving his arms in front of the Mouth, but nothing, no response.

The MouthMan scanned Wee Dave's passport and with a clunk and a heave, the door was open for them. Closing the door, the MouthMan thought, *They're right, what a useless existence I have come to. Bring back the days when I was in the League of the Sky!*

After hearing the door slam shut behind them, Jamie said, 'Let's do the stairs.'

'Serious? It's seventy-odd floors!' Wee Dave shouted, but Jamie was already gone. He looked at the mountain of steps in front of him and thought it impossible, but *I'll do it until Jamie stops.* The two kids were running joyfully up each flight, step by step, then two at a time as the pace quickened. Getting to the thirtieth floor, Wee Dave's legs were in so much pain, but he would not stop until Jamie stopped. He was slowly catching up, but his legs, his feet, his back...

On to the fiftieth floor and the distance was still the same. Wee Dave's heart was beating like the clappers, he felt as though his heart would jump out at any moment, the sweat running from every pore on his young body, but he could not stop, he must run through the pain, his legs, oh his feet.

By the sixtieth floor he could see Jamie slowing, he was catching up with each step. Nearly there, they're gonna make it, but who will win? All of a sudden, Jamie's trailing ankle hit a step, obviously too tired to lift the leg high enough for the next step, and Wee Dave heard the bang of a knee as Jamie fell.

Within a second Wee Dave was past, he was gonna win, until he felt his shoe being grabbed from behind and he tripped arse over heel. The two of them were up in a shot, knowing it was going to be head-to-head until the very end, until that very last step.

The final flight, Wee Dave could see the door in front, but to his side Jamie was matching each stride. Reaching out for the door, which was within arm's length by now… He could feel Jamie's shoulder brush against him, leaning into him. Wee Dave pushed back slightly as they both shoved through the door at the same time, falling to the floor and rolling around in fits of laughter.

'I won!'

'I won!'

Punching and kicking each other on the ground, they continued to argue over who was the winner until they slowly got their breath back and their hearts had resumed at a normal pace. Looking up, Wee Dave noticed Slyme's father staring at them from outside their designated field, arms folded and shaking his head in disgust. Quickly getting to his feet he brushed himself off, grabbed Jamie and stormed past Slyme's father, all three showing no sign of acknowledgement towards the other.

'You see the look on his face?' Jamie asked.

'Yeah, he hates us, mate,' Wee Dave whispered. 'Ever since you came to the team and I haven't been spending as much time with Slyme.'

'That's his own fault, innit?'

'Yeah, more interested in PlayStations.'

'And eating!' Jamie laughed after giving a much more plump Slyme a look from head to toe.

Wee Dave knew he shouldn't laugh, but Slyme had become morbidly obese by now and his football skills were horrendous. It wasn't the football that annoyed Wee Dave, Slyme had become more and more like his father, short and sharp, blaming everyone but himself. Shouting. Shouting. Shouting. Demands. Commands. Demand. Command. Wee Dave tried to help him but he was told in no uncertain terms to 'stick your advice where the sun don't shine!' So they became further and further apart, and the team hated Slyme because he was turning into his father. Throwing his toys out when he didn't get what he wanted. Sad times.

'Shame, he was always such a good player when we were young,' Wee Dave replied. Then looking to the stands, through the thousands of agents, coaches and scouts alike, he spotted Fergus in his usual seat at the back corner. He smiled and gave his customary wave, which was returned with warmth.

'It's so nice that he keeps coming,' Jamie said. 'He doesn't have to, but still, there he is, every week!'

'Aye, he's a legend!' After a moment's silence, Wee Dave grabbed a ball and asked, 'Head tennis?'

'Sure, but this time, we'll do two headers each time, see what happens.'

'Sounds good,' Wee Dave replied and threw the ball towards Jamie, who glanced it into the air and with the second header it was directed back to Wee Dave, who returned the compliment.

'Shit! We're with Slyme,' Wee Dave muttered to Jamie after the teams had been sorted.

Every player from the League of the Youth had been invited to play in the try-outs for the Amateur Leagues. They would play a six-team seven-a-side tournament, where two games would take place at one time, while two teams rested. The tournaments were arranged in different time slots with Wee Dave and co. finding themselves in the third time slot, from 13:00–15:00. The try-outs were held from 09:00–23:00 on Saturday and Sunday, with over 600 players attempting to make it. Two hours to show you're better than hundreds of other players. You must impress, Wee Dave; you must be outstanding, Jamie.

'No worries, we've carried him this far, ain't we?' Jamie said, still smiling and relaxed. 'All we can do is our best, no more. What will be, will be.'

Pulling their green bibs on, they ran to the first field. Bouncing up and down, bringing his knees to his chin as he did so, Wee Dave tried to get rid of the last bit of nerves. He looked around the rest of the team, not knowing any of them, if they were any good, if they were world-beaters, everyone would be knees and socks to him in the next few hours. Looking across, they played against a red team in the first match.

'I'm striker,' Slyme said when the team had gathered together to do positions, trudging off to the halfway line to start.

'Don't worry about him, it's all he's good at anyway,' Wee Dave said to the rest before asking what positions they play.

'Defence,' said one.

'Goalie,' said another.

After a few moments Wee Dave jogged towards the left wing, being the only left-footer in the team, and Jamie was on the right of a 1:2:3:1 formation. Before Smite, goalkeepers were seen as nothing, they were not important enough to be included in formations such as 4:4:2 or 4:3:3.

Touch, pass. Touch, pass. Touch, pass. The Greens started the game controlling possession, not wanting to make an early mistake, not wanting to risk. Then Wee Dave found himself in space, and taking a few touches towards the defender he dropped his shoulder to the right and jinking to the left he sailed past with ease. First one-on-one battle, only one winner. Gliding up the field like a swan, the centre-back came across to tackle him, leaving Slyme in acres of space. Waiting until the last moment, Wee Dave slipped him through, one-on-one with the goalie. Should be easy!

But the ball bounced off Slyme and the Reds gained possession. Wee Dave was back behind the ball like a whippet, defensive transition the only thing on his mind and sliding in from the side, he knocked the ball out of play, stopping a dangerous counterattack.

'Oi! Wee Dave,' Slyme yelled. 'Easier next time!'

Thumbs up, continue playing, no need to answer to Slyme's whinging.

Down the right, Jamie in space this time, rolling the ball one way, then the other, nutmeg, through the legs, bursting down the right wing with Wee Dave trying to keep up on the far side. He was still in awe of the ease at which Jamie could manoeuvre the ball and the speed at which it was carried. Jamie hit the ball low and hard across the goal, Wee Dave sliding in at the back post, trying to get his toe on the end of it, but it was just out of his reach. So close.

Wee Dave applauded the good play, both making eye contact, smiling, already knowing that they had the better of their opponents.

'Why would you not cut that back!?' screamed Slyme. 'I was in so much space!'

Jamie and Wee Dave looked at each other, rolled their eyes to the sky and continued the match.

The next ball was played from centre-back straight to Slyme's feet, who instantly controlled it, and after hearing calls from Jamie and Wee Dave who were in acres of space on the wings, he decided to ignore them and let loose with a right-foot strike which sailed high and wide.

'NO MOVEMENT!' he screamed, slamming his fist on the ground.

'Calm down, Slyme, we were there for you, have a look next time,' Jamie said, almost embarrassed at the sight of him.

'No you weren't,' he argued back.

'Just ignore him,' Wee Dave shouted from the other side. 'Play our usual game, remember?'

After working hard, battling and winning possession the Greens had chance after chance, only for them to be wasted by Slyme, who was only too keen to blame someone else.

Finally, Jamie rolled the ball to Slyme on a plate, he tripped over his own feet but somehow bundled the ball past the goalkeeper.

Wee Dave, Jamie and the rest of the Green team breathed a collective sigh of relief and clenched their fists after dominating for so long.

Meanwhile, Slyme ran the length of the spectators holding one finger up, then pointing to himself with both thumbs he mimed the words: 'Number 1, me, Number 1.'

It was much the same for the rest of the match, and the rest of the try-out for that matter. There is always that one player who wants the credit for everything and unfortunately it was Slyme. He scored the most goals, and he made sure everyone knew this at the final whistle.

The coaches, scouts and agents gathered on the field, trying to introduce themselves to the players, but the biggest crowd was around Jamie and Wee Dave. They looked to each other and laughed – of course they had played well, but they did not expect this. The circle was closing in on them from all angles and they found themselves in the centre of a thousand-man scrum… they were trapped, unable to move as fingers poked at their heads.

Wee Dave got to his knees and crawled through the first set of legs, taking a knee to the ribs but knowing no other way to escape. He could hear Jamie close behind, scuttling along, trying to get free. When they did get out, they ran straight up to Fergus, who was smiling back at them.

'Look at that swarm of idiots down there,' Jamie laughed. 'Fighting and elbowing over nothing.' Then, cupping his hands, he shouted, 'There's no one there, you morons! We're up here!'

'How did we do?' Wee Dave whispered to Fergus.

'Are you kidding me? Does that not answer your question?' he said as he pointed down to the gathered thousands. 'They're all for you!'

'But do you not think…'

'David,' Fergus cut him off. 'Trust me, you were awesome, you'll have plenty of offers.'

Wee Dave was content, but not happy. He had lost the ball after dribbling into two players when there was a simple pass on. This resulted in the opposition team scoring and he was furious at himself.

'So which one is Coach Jeremy?' he asked. Fergus had told them that Coach Jeremy was one of the best coaches in the Amateur League, he was very friendly and they would learn a lot from him.

'See the man at the very back corner, close to the water tank, with the red hat?' He pointed.

'Yeah…' Wee Dave and Jamie said in unison.

'Well if you look two to the left of him… the fella all in black… that's him.'

'What? That small fella?' asked Jamie.

'Yes, the small fella.'

'Sure he don't look like much.' Jamie replied.

'And I do?' said Fergus, and raising his thick white eyebrows, he took off his bowl hat and bowed to them. When Wee Dave gave him the once over he noticed how old Fergus looked, his skin drooping at his eyes which were all the more magnified by his thick glasses, the thin wisp of white hair around the sides and back of his head more clumpy than smooth, and the bald spot on top covered in purple blotches.

'Don't judge a book by its cover!' he said after firmly replacing his hat where it belonged and grabbing his walking stick. He creaked onto his feet to stretch, still showing them that wise old smile.

'Whatever you say, we'll do it,' Wee Dave determined. They stayed with Fergus for a while longer as the players for the next try-outs were arriving and the 'swarm of idiots' were making their way back to the stands. They put their hoods up to hide themselves from the paparazzi.

As the field was clearing, Wee Dave caught a glance of Coach Jeremy, who was still on the field in heated discussions with a fat man who looked like a penguin. Wee Dave could not see the face of the penguin, but there was a lot of finger-waving and it seemed a very animated conversation. It ended with a resigned look from Coach Jeremy, who was holding both hands face-forward while mouthing the words 'Okay, okay,' and nodding his head up and down. After reaching his hand out for the penguin to shake, Coach Jeremy took his place in the stands and as the penguin turned to stare after him, Wee Dave was looking at the rat-like features of Mr Slyme, who seemed relatively pleased with himself.

Leaning over to Jamie, he whispered, 'Let's get outta here.'

'Yeah, let's go, see ye later Fergus.'

'Bye,' Fergus replied, turning from the match and giving them a wave.

'Do you think…' started Wee Dave.

Fergus rolled his eyes. 'You'll be fine,' he stated and waved them away.

'Okay, thanks Fergus, see ya later,' he smiled and trekked after Jamie, who as usual had sprinted ahead of him, winning the race.

The tip, tap, tip, tap, tip, tap of quick feet was heard all the way down the steps, Wee Dave jumping the bottom three, four and then five steps of each flight, trying to catch Jamie. Bursting through the doors without a glance at the MouthMan, he swung his leg over the bike and pedalled! Pedal like crazy with Jamie just in vision. Pedal faster and he's catching up, the breeze hitting his hair, coughing up the phlegm, the pollution, legs in pain, thighs, quads, keep going, come on, keep going!

One last burst from Wee Dave was not enough as Jamie skidded to a stop a few metres in front of him at the Bridge, both bent over double from their efforts.

'Right,' breath, breath. 'See you tomorrow?'

'Give us a sec,' Jamie replied, holding his hand out, heaving deep breaths. 'Uh… tomorrow I've work all day. We'll have to wait till next week, maybe during the week? Meet ya at the field?'

'Hmm… I've a good bitta homework for next week. Saturday then?'

'Aye, sounds good mate. See ya then.' Jamie waved and circled over the Bridge, Wee Dave watching after him. They were not to know that this was the last time they'd see each other for two years.

Still ten people in front of me, thought Wee Dave in agonising boredom when he got to the back of the line, having taken his shot and collected his football. *Just let us play football, for Smite's sake!*

'Good strike, Slyme,' Coach John shouted, after a shot which was not even on target. The two boys in front of Wee Dave started to giggle and playfully fight with each other. Coach John's face turned red with anger, and frothing at the mouth like a pit bull he shouted, 'Oi, you two, stop messing around! Gimme five laps of the field!' The two boys dropped their heads and commenced jogging around the field, although halfway around they started to laugh and hit each other again.

'Why do these boys not listen? Why do they keep messing around?' Coach John mumbled under his breath, but Wee Dave heard every word of it.

Probably because we're bored, he thought. *Still five players before my go*. His mind wandered…

Where did it all go wrong? Why was he standing in line waiting to kick a ball once, only to trudge to the back of the line and wait another five minutes before he could have another go?

Everything had gone according to plan after the try-outs, receiving almost a thousand letters, but looking for just one, the one from Coach Jeremy of The Stars. And there it was, in the fifty-third envelope. The rest of the letters were thrown into the air out of jubilation, and as they floated back to the ground it was like something out of an episode of *The Crystal Maze*. Mum and Dad smiled with pride at their boy.

'I can't wait to tell Jamie,' he shouted. 'I hope he's made it.'

'I'm sure he has,' Dad said, winking and pointing to his nose, as if he knew something already. Wee Dave smiled and ran over to them, arms open wide to embrace them in a huge hug.

But that Saturday, when he cycled to the Bridge to meet Jamie at their usual spot, at the normal time, the Bridge was raised with no way to cross. Wee Dave had never seen the Bridge like this before and didn't know what it meant, he didn't know what to do. So he did nothing. Nothing but wait for the next four hours, looking over the Bridge to see if there were any signs of life.

'Dad,' he shouted, leaving his bike on the grass out front, 'the Bridge is raised, I've been there all day.'

Dad looked up from the paper. 'You haven't seen the news, have you son?'

'No, what's happened?' Wee Dave asked, running behind Dad to have a look at the *Evening Bull*. He stared at the headline:

VIOLENCE HITS AN ALL-TIME HIGH IN LOWERTON.

'But there is no violence!' Wee Dave pleaded. 'I'm there all the time and there's nothing.'

'David, it is a very dangerous place. Just because you know Jamie, does not mean you know the millions of other people in Lowerton. People die because of the violence every day, sure we see it in the news.'

'So what does it mean? Why have they put the Bridge up?'

Dad closed the paper before Wee Dave could read more. 'It means that we cannot go into Lowerton anymore, so you'll just have to train at the Park.'

'But Dad,' he started, furious at the injustice and wondering why the world had turned against him.

'But nothing, son,' he said, matter-of-factly. 'What can we do about it?'

'We can…' Wee Dave trailed off. Dad was right of course, there was nothing they could do. 'Does it say when it will reopen?'

'It only says the Bridge will come down when the violence ends.'

'And what about Jamie? What about The Stars? He must have made it, he's way better than I am!'

'David,' Dad said in a serious tone. 'There is nothing we can do.'

As Wee Dave came back to the present he realised he was the next in line for a shot. Putting his ball down, he passed to Coach John, who stopped the ball with his foot, looked at him expectantly and after getting no response, put both arms out to the side and yelled, 'Which way?'

'Oh yeah! Ummmm… right!' Wee Dave called back, which resulted in Coach John laying the ball off for Wee Dave to run and strike with his right foot. The ball sailed into the top corner and Wee Dave trudged after it, collecting it in one arm and joining the back of the line… back to his thoughts.

He remembered the first few weeks of training with The Stars, with Coach Jeremy. Just like Fergus, Coach Jeremy loved to coach during matches, putting certain conditions on the games to ensure that there was guided learning for the players. He made each player feel good about themselves, he allowed them to learn at their own pace and had fun with them. He was approachable, he was likeable and Wee Dave enjoyed the few weeks they had together.

What he couldn't believe was the sight of Slyme playing with The Stars. How did he get there? He was not at the same level as the rest of the players and his lack of effort had cost them their first two matches, with him blaming everyone but himself. With the team losing two matches in a row there was uproar from the parents, led by Slyme's father of course, who complained about the coaching style and demanded that they do more fitness and more shooting like the professionals.

The other parents were afraid of Mr Slyme so they followed suit, backing him without saying a word, just nodding in agreement. The parents' revolt led to Coach Jeremy walking away. Being a normal working man, using his spare time to coach football in a

154

voluntary position, the pressure had become too much to bear. As all great coaches do, he brought the stresses home to his family and it had become too much for them to take.

This was what his letter to the parents said. Some parents believed the letter, some thought that he had been sacked, others that he had been bribed.

Either way, he had gone and to the boys it didn't matter *how* he had gone, they blamed themselves for the mess that they had caused. It led to Coach John taking the reins and he was only too happy to comply to the parents'/Slyme's demands and send them for fitness, discipline them with laps and push-ups, and finish with a line of shooting. The parents were delighted at this new, more professional style of coaching which taught the boys discipline.

But what about the boys? The players? Sure it didn't matter about their opinions, as long as the parents and coaches are happy. As long as they're winning games…

And the parents and coaches did all they could to win games. It was common to see them hurling abuse at the referee, running onto the field and threatening them with knives, machetes and machine guns. Anywhere else in Society these crimes would be met with fines, community service or prison, but the competitive nature of sport made this behaviour acceptable.

All Wee Dave wanted to do was play football, but the crowd trouble led to most games being cancelled or postponed, meaning less and less football every week. A typical ninety-minute game would be thirty minutes of football, with the other sixty minutes spent controlling the parents and coaches.

Oh… back to the present and it was time for Wee Dave's next shot. He rolled the ball to Coach John, pointing to the left this time, and with all his might he unleashed his anger and frustration on the ball, which thundered off the crossbar and rebounded to hit Coach John in the back of the head. He looked around dazed at first, a few of the boys in line unable to hold in snorts of laughter.

'That's three laps, David!'

Wee Dave puffed his cheeks and began the jog, tears dropping down his cheeks, thinking of the car journeys to training, the Slymes boring him with their talk of City and the League of the Sky, the incredible atmosphere from the past weekend.

He sniffed, wiped his eyes, but he could not rid himself of the never-ending tears.

It had been six months since the day the Bridge raised and it was still in that upright position. Wee Dave kept his eye on the *Bull Standard* for signs of it reopening, he called Fergus who was as dumbfounded as he was, he asked in School but the resounding cry from Stout was usually something along the lines of...

'You must think onwards and upwards, young man. Upperton is where you want to be.'

Stout had become so big that he looked like a hot air balloon with arms and legs. He missed the days when he and Slyme made fun of Stout, but Slyme had his PlayStation friends now, Dave had no one.

'OKAY, THAT'S TIME!' Coach John shouted. The boys jogged in to form a circle around him, Dave joining at the back, his face bloated by now from his tears. 'Clean yourself up, boy,' Coach John said. 'Look at the state of you!' Wee Dave wiped his arm across his face, still sniffling while the rest sat in silence, listening to the usual post-training talk of how the boys 'need to listen more' and 'to stop messing around'.

When the sermon was finished, Wee Dave got his bag and walked off to the side, head drooping low, bottom lip still quivering.

'You not coming with us?' Slyme called after him.

'Nah, I'm gonna walk,' came the reply. As he walked slowly from the Park, his head was full, bloated with the same thoughts and worries which had haunted him for the last six months.

I wonder if Jamie is okay.

Why can't he have a phone? Then I could contact him.

He can't afford it!

I'm sure he's okay.

I hope he's okay.

He's probably not okay. The violence is very bad there now, worse than ever.

He's definitely not okay. If he was okay he would have found a way to cross the Bridge.

Why can't they just let us across? There's no violence!

Bloody violence, ruins everything.

No fun, where has the fun gone? No play on a playground. No ball games.

I miss the Glory Years.

I miss my best friend.

I miss The Buccaneers.

Shaking his head of his thoughts, Wee Dave realised that his autopilot walking had taken him to the Bridge. He looked across, longing to be on the other side, wondering what was going on. Leaning on the wall he looked across the river into the dead town, no movement with the exception of rubbish flying in the wind. He followed one piece for a while as it drifted over Lowerton.

Then a flash of light in the distance. What could that be?

Must be an airplane... but the light had disappeared. Maybe a shooting star, yeah... probably a shooting star.

Except the same flash happened again, in the exact same place. Wee Dave did not take his eyes off that spot for the next five minutes but nothing happened. Waiting. Waiting for nothing but...

There it was again, only longer this time. It was a shape of some sort. What was that shape? Frowning, he took his bag off his back and fetched his iPad.

Binoculars app.

Zoom in.

Too dark to see. I know, I'll video it.

Zoom in, wait, wait patiently, patience is the—

FLASH.

Got it. Recorded.

Open the video on the iPad. Slow motion, slooooooooow. Too slow.

Play.

Damn. Too quick. Missed it.

Rewind.

Slow motion. Wait for it and...

FLASH!

PAUSE!

What the hell?

Frowning at the freeze-frame, Wee Dave could tell that the light had come from a shape in the mountains, but it was still extremely difficult to make out what this shape was. After some zooming and sharpening with the photo editor, the blurred image turned into the shape of a person. It must have been 100ft tall. It was the largest statue that Wee Dave had ever seen. The statue was pointing its finger directly at him, and as Wee Dave swiped his finger down on the screen, he was staring at the unmistakable and intimidating face of Mr Smite.

Chapter 14

Jamie

Dear Jamie,

We regret to inform you that you will no longer be invited to train with the STARS and we must make you aware of the specialisation involved in the game of football.

Ever since the great Mr Smite and Mr Sky were leaders in our Society and in football, it has been decided that football should be played solely by boys, giving them a greater chance to reach their potential and play in the League of the Sky. Girls have their own sports that they specialise in, giving them a better chance to move to Upperton.

We were unaware of your gender until it was brought to our attention by another parent, who quite rightly fears for his son's future. We hope that this simple mistake, one that anyone could make, will not affect you greatly and we wish you all the success in the future.

Regards
The STARS

Jamie couldn't keep her eyes off the letter, one single water balloon dropping from her eye and landing on 'Jamie', the damp circle on the page slowly getting bigger and made even worse by the rainfall which followed. She crumpled the letter and threw it in the bin, reaching for the acceptance letter she had received only two days before, a letter she had hung on her wall, so proud of herself for making the team, and tore it to shreds.

It was Friday, almost a week since the try-outs, since the last time she saw her best mate, Wee Dave. Without him she could not even have read the letters, he had taught her so many things that he had taken for granted and had learned in School, such as Maths and English, but for Jamie these were an effort. She lived for spending time with Wee Dave, he was the best thing that had ever happened to her, he was her Paradise.

As Jamie sat on the floor, knees tucked up to her chin, rocking backwards and forwards and staring at the scrunched up mess in the bin. She thought how she had always been mistaken for a boy, obviously a side effect of growing up in the rough and tumble streets of Lowerton. She even suspected that Wee Dave thought she was a boy, but who cared? What did it matter if you were a boy, a girl, black, white, small, tall, fat, thin… everyone is a human being.

But Jamie was not educated and did not understand that there was a place for each person in Society. Even for her. She was the bottom of Society, the Scum. But she didn't know it.

Having grown up in Lowerton, she was always grafting, living from day to day, just about getting by and taking care of her Granda. From six years old Jamie was delivering newspapers, collecting them from the corner shop at 08:00 and lugging them with her to Building 326. When she first started her paper round, the bag was bigger than her, the straps digging into her shoulder leaving red marks, the mark of the Devil, the mark of pain. But she found a way to deliver to every house in the 100-storey block.

After finishing her shift, usually around 18:00, she would walk back to the shop with some of the other workers to receive their pay of half a loaf each.

'This bread,' a lad said to her one day. 'It's ratten! Can't even get a lick o' butter for her!'

'I wash 'er down with water,' she replied.

'Sure that water's stankin as well, pure muck from the sewers!'

Jamie knew this but what else could she do? This was all she and her Granda had, and she felt privileged for the work, knowing that without it they'd be on the streets. Her Granda was fifty-three years old now, far too old and weak to worry about work. And with her Ma dying in childbirth, and her Da dying only a few years later, she was the sole breadwinner in the family.

It was in her second month on the job when she met her love, she was introduced to Paradise.

'Here Wee Man, wa's yer name?' some gruff looking lad of about ten shouted.

'Jamie... S'craic?'

'You doin' much after work?'

'Nah, just straight back home wi' me granda.'

'Well here… we've a game down the Green if you fancy it?'

'The Green?'

'Aye, meet us at the shap later and I'll show ye.'

Later that day Jamie took her half loaf to Granda, quickly ate with him and told him she was going out to play. When she arrived at the shop there were a bunch of other lads waiting, some tall, some small, but all bare to the bone.

'Right, let's go,' said the gruff looking lad from earlier, waving them to follow. Jamie took her place at the tail of the group as they walked down the trodden path of leaves, down the concrete oval and onto the beautiful green grass of the football field. The Green. Football. The love of her life. Paradise.

After this day she spent every spare second thinking about football, even while she was delivering she was thinking what moves to use later to trick the defenders. She would begin her shifts earlier each day to allow for more time to play, but in the early days, the boys at the Green were too big and strong so she preferred to play on the street outside the apartment, her and a random neighbour throwing down T-shirts for goals and using bottles or bottle tops for a ball, playing until 01:00 every night. They would have played later but, you know, work!

It didn't take Jamie long to be down at the Green every night playing against the 'big oafs', as she called them. She was always a cheeky little bugger.

On Jamie's eighth birthday she got the best present she could ever ask for, she got offered a job as a cleaner, guaranteed fourteen hours per day. Obviously, getting paid in real money meant she had to start paying taxes, but she could still just about afford half a loaf of bread for her and Granda.

It was around this time that she met Wee Dave, a young and handsome boy from Middleton, and unlike the rest of the toffs, he seemed to like playing football with her. The Middleton boys she had seen had always kept their heads down and had been scared to leave their cars. She had so much fun that day at her Da's charity match and she never forgot about him, but she assumed that he had forgotten her because he did not come back. Like all the other boys from Middleton, he was probably playing his computer games.

Not long after the charity match, Jamie met a man from the papers who promised her extra work. She was only too pleased to do this work and even though it was voluntary, she was told it would 'take her places'.

'Now, it's important you get the good photos Jamie,' he said. 'Photos that show the harmony within Lowerton, groups having their drinks, especially the ones watching the football, outside pubs, you know the craic…'

'Of course, boss,' she replied, and this little square box became her life, never seeing the actual photos but in the knowledge that she was doing a good deed. Plus, her boss usually gave her a chicken wing as a tip and this was kept for her and Granda for after the Buccaneers match each Saturday.

She was unaware that these photos of men celebrating and cheering ran under the headlines of '*THUGS AND HOOLIGANS*', and even if she did see, she would not have been able to read it.

As well as the 'good photos', Jamie got snaps of the dead, the statistics which according to the *Bull Standard* 'had been taken by the violence of Lowerton'. In reality, these people were dying of hunger, dying from the freezing cold of their own homes, a lot of them resorting to taking their own lives to avoid the suffering.

With this camera Jamie became well known across Lowerton, becoming more confident around others, and she found herself going to the Green more often to play against the bigger lads. The best thing about the Green was being able to play with a real football, it made her feel closer to the stars of the Buccaneers and she would pretend to be one of them, usually Stan. She found herself there after work every night, usually the first to arrive and the last to leave. And then...

There he was again, she was not sure how many months had passed but there he was, trying to do some form of keepy-ups with a ball. Her heart fluttered and she could not hold her excitement in.

'YOU!' she screamed. They played the most amazing game together, had wild piles of craic before a call from Wee Dave's dad took him away.

'You better make sure it's not as long next time,' she winked at him.

The year that followed was pure bliss, Jamie spent lots of time with Wee Dave, helping him become a better footballer with him repaying the favour by teaching Jamie some basic maths and how to read. At the back of her mind, she knew this was all too good to be true, she knew she would never need to read or do maths, but it seemed to make Wee Dave happy, so it made her happy.

Then Fergus came into her life, got her signed up for a team and while playing in the League of the Youth she was able to eat twice per day, and keep leftovers for Granda.

Life cannot get much better than this! she thought.

But it did, the local elections were just around the corner and hundreds of thousands of people from Lowerton were guaranteed work on a new project if Mr Stout was elected as Governor. These elections were held every four years, and nobody in Lowerton ever took much notice of them.

'Sure, what can they do for us?' was the usual cry.

But Mr Stout provided a ray of sunshine for the Scum. *'DELIVERING JOBS AND SAVING LIVES'* the slogan read from the huge banners which were attached to every building in Lowerton. When Election Day came everyone vowed to go and vote for Mr Stout and Lowerton would be saved.

Along with the great news about Lowerton, Jamie had been guaranteed football for the next two years, having signed a contract with the Stars, Coach Jeremy telling her that she was 'the best player he had seen in a very long time'.

'Will I ever get a chance to play for The Buccaneer Falls?' she asked after the try-out.

'The Buccaneers?' he said, incredulously. 'Son, you have the talent to go all the way to the top, all the way to the League of the Sky. Don't set your standards at The Buccaneers,' he sniggered and walked off.

Jamie's heart pounded. *Did he just call me son?* she thought, but she brushed it off. *It won't matter, everything will be fine.*

The day after the try-outs Mr Stout had been elected as Governor, which brought much joy to Lowerton, and to celebrate his triumph he bought beers and wines, vodka and whiskey, and everyone had a night full of fun and laughter, dancing and merriment, living for the moment, worries taken off their shoulders at the prospect of well-paid jobs and guaranteed food.

A life.

Sweat was dripping from Jamie's head, and as she looked around at the thousands of other construction workers, she could see how tired they were, the stench of stale sweat filling the air. She could barely feel her fingers through the thin pair of gloves which had been provided, but she was only minutes away from clock off time and getting her daily pay.

She had never been paid this much before in her life, and was guaranteed eighteen hours of work per day, along with all of the other workers on site. It was incredible and Mr Stout really did deliver on his promises. She watched on as other workers took their lunchbreak, workers with hands black as coal stuffing slices of bread into their mouths. Having done this on many occasions, a bitter taste of mud came to her tongue and she was on the verge of chundering.

She climbed down from her twenty-foot ladder, knees wobbling at each rung, and felt a sense of relief when she got to the ground, although she was still shaking like a leaf. Taking a deep breath and turning her head, she witnessed a much higher ladder sliding on the marble surface, a piercing scream coming from the man at the top as he dropped head first into the gravel below.

Another one bites the dust.

The workers did not take much notice as the claw swivelled around, lowering itself as it did so and clenched its grip on the man, lifting him high into the air and catapulting him over the side of the mountain, well out of the way.

Jamie watched as the body sailed through the night sky until it was out of her vision. Another sigh, a tired yawn and she slapped herself in the face, forcing herself to keep her eyes open.

Grabbing her name badge she trudged over to the MouthMan to wait for her shift to finish. If she clocked out early, she would not have got full pay and she did not finish until 23:00. It was 22:58 and there was a crowd of workers arriving, clocking in for the night shift, while the day shift workers had to hang around for two minutes, not much chitter-chatter as they were all battered and beaten. At 23:00 there was a mass brawl to get to the MouthMan to collect their five credits, which was just enough to buy Jamie lunch and dinner for the next day, still always keeping a slice for her Granda.

The last year had been eighteen hours of work, with a one-hour cycle to and from home, thirty minutes spent telling her Granda about the goings-on of the day and three and a half hours sleep. But she got paid five credits per day, so how could she complain?

Alternating her hands back and forth between her pockets and the handlebars, her breath rising in front of her eyes, she could not wait to get to her Paradise, the warm cup of hot water which Granda prepared for her every night, and then under the covers of bed.

The streets were full of cyclists doing the same trip home and Jamie remembered how she used to walk these streets in the past, these streets which were lined with homeless people, sitting by fires, warming their hands, smoking their cigarettes and begging for food. Mr Stout had done such a great job getting these people off the streets and into work.

The death toll due to hunger and homelessness had dropped significantly, so Mr Stout was clearly a man to deliver on his promises.

Jamie turned into Centre Street. Each building was covered with banners of the great Mr Stout. *So they should be*, she thought. *He has done more for this place than anyone in the history of The City.*

As she got closer to home she saw the different shades of grey smog coming from Middleton. There had not been a car in sight since the building work had begun, yet the pollution levels of

Lowerton had risen to an all-time high. Jamie heard the coughing and sputtering of a fellow cyclist in front and the wind carried the slimy ball of green directly into her face. Wiping it with the sleeve of her jumper, she just wanted to get home as quickly as possible.

Leaving the bike at the side of her building, she hoped that it would still be there in a few hours so she did not have to pay for a new one, and entered her apartment block. When she walked in, her Granda was asleep on the floor.

Thank Smite, she thought, she was so knackered and glad that she could just crash.

The next morning she woke with her work clothes still on, crept past her Granda, who was still asleep, and found her bike from the day before.

Good start!

Twenty hours later, after a normal day and a normal cycle home, she opened the door to her apartment block and nearly threw up with the stench of bad meat. Slowly walking up the stairs to the top floor, the smell got stronger. When she got to her apartment she could hear a buzzing noise from inside, like a low-flying airplane.

What is that? she frowned.

After opening the door she gasped at the smell and then the sight of her Granda, lying in the same place she had left him, but now surrounded by a million flies, battling to get to his skin, to his eyes, to anywhere they could. Jamie had to slam the door before vomiting everywhere.

Mum... Dad... Wee Dave... Now Granda! I have lost everyone. What have I done to deserve this?

'I went to see The Buccaneers last night, Jamie,' Billy shouted from the top of the ladder. After so many falls and deaths from falling off ladders, Mr Stout had very kindly provided assistance by placing a worker at the bottom to hold tight, and in this case, it was Jamie.

'Yeah?' she shouted. 'I ain't seen 'em in ages, any new players?'

'Aye, there's this one kid, youngest player to ever play, same age as you I reckon.'

'Any use?'

'Nah, 'parrently he's havin' a nightmare season, or so the reg'lars are sayin'.'

'Sure give 'im a bitta time and I'm sure 'e'll bed in, they always do.'

'It's diffrent nai tho,' Billy shouted back. 'Hardly any fans there anymore.'

'Aye, sure they're all 'ere now, ain't they? Workin' on this friggin' statue!'

Billy slowly climbed down the ladder, and as he got near the bottom said a bit more quietly, 'Careful what you're shouting Jamie, could get inter ba'r if someone ears ya.'

'Awk, I know Billy bai, but I've lost ma temper wif fis,' Jamie answered, first pointing at the statue and then waving her hand around the construction site. 'It's takin our lives away and for waa? We're still livin' the same, naffin's improved.'

'Come on now Jamie, we have work and pay. That's more than we deserve, coming from where we do.'

'What we deserve!? Billy, what were you promised when ya took this jab?'

'What do you mean?'

'Well, I was told tha' I'd be in a lovely big affice, doing ano'er cleaning jab, getting better pay! I din't fink I'd be out 'ere climbin' ladders and dodgin' boulders. You see poor Gordy las' week, he

170

gat hit so hard in the head that it buried him under the ground, they still haven't removed the stone. Tha's nat cleanin' mate.'

'But we get paid more, don' we?'

'Sure we do, but don' we 'ave to put it straight back inter their packets, buying those loaves every day! We get our well earned money, and then 'ave to give it straight back!' Jamie threw one of the stones she had picked from the ground over the cliff, utterly frustrated at the way things had worked out.

'You don' have ta, do ya?' Billy replied. Billy was always calm around Jamie, trying to make her see sense, and this usually worked, but today was different. 'Ere, I tell you wa',' he said sensing that he had not helped her. 'What if I get us tickets for the game next week? We're in the Cup Final, it'll be like old times.'

Jamie, who was in the middle of a crouch to find her next rock, froze halfway down and looked up to Billy, mouth agape.

'We're in the Cup Final? Again?' she asked.

'I know I couln't believe it eever, we're on for ano'er double!'

'No way,' Jamie shouted. 'No way!' she repeated, and running over to Billy as fast as she could, she leapt into his arms.

'Are you being serious?' she asked again after letting him go.

'Anestly mate,' he replied. 'Nat as good as before, when we used ta go, the football's definitely nat as good, but still… a Cup Final.'

'Sure, all the bais who played before are workin' down 'ere, I saw Stan only the o'er day holdin' a ladder for yer man Barry, 'member thon big striker we had.'

'Oh aye, he scored some headers, din't he?'

'Aye but Stan, me and ma best mate used ta love 'im. See when we played at the Green, I'd always pretend I was Stan, scoring goals fer fun…' Jamie trailed off at the thought of how she wanted to be

Stan, be on the same field as him. Little did she know that it would actually come true… The only difference being that the field was a construction site and the football a paintbrush and a ladder.

'But seriously Jamie, it's nat like it was when we went, the noise ain't anywhere near the same and we've a loada toffs from Middleton comin' across in a bus ta play!'

'But we're on for ano'er double,' and raising her fist she shouted, 'MON BUCCANEERS!'

There seemed to be an awakening across the construction site as other workers started to cry…

'MON BUCCANEERS!'

'MON BUCCANEERS!'

A rendition of an old Falls song started to echo around the building site, one young man forgetting he was holding the ladder and putting his fist in the air caused another great fall and another statistic, but it was a brief moment of joy for those who were at work.

As the song died a voice boomed over the loudspeaker. 'BACK TO WORK!'

'D'you mind goin' up this time? My knees ain't like they used ta be,' Billy said after being brought back down to earth.

'Aye, no worries, I ain't bin up this week.'

'Careful mate, we're a good ten feet higher than last week.'

'Still on his knuckles though, ain't we? For Smite's sake, this is huge,' Jamie said, and after a breath started to ascend the rungs.

'I left the paint jus' to the right,' Billy shouted from below, and on the scaffolding, which still covered the entire monument, sat a pot of black paint, roller inside.

'Gat it,' Jamie shouted back as she climbed on to the scaffolding to continue where Billy had left off.

Two hours later she was still on the knuckle of the third finger when she heard the horn go for time. She put the roller into the pot and wiped the sweat from her head, looking into the distance at another smaller hill that she had never noticed before.

She frowned. Was this double vision? After all, she was knackered.

Carefully she climbed down the ladder, knees wobbling all the way, and after getting to the bottom she asked Billy.

'Here, have you ever seen that mountain over there?' She pointed.

'What mountain? There's no mountain there.'

'I jus' saw it from the tap, there's another mountain beside us.'

'It's dark Jamie, you're knackered, there's naffin' there.'

'I'm tellin' ya, there's another mountain there. Let's go and look.'

She grabbed Billy by the arm, climbed over the 'no entry' ropes and walked towards where she was pointing.

'Ya see,' she said as they got closer, and right enough, you could see the outline of a slightly smaller mountain as they passed the trees.

'Jamie, I don't think we should be here,' Billy whispered, staying a little back from Jamie, voice shaking with nerves.

'Nansense, 'mon,' she replied, grabbing Billy by the sleeve and dragging him down the winding path.

Billy pulled his hand back. Jamie looked at him and his face was as white as a ghost.

'Jamie, I am nat goin' down there, look!' he moaned, pointing to the top of the mountain. Jamie followed Billy's finger. She could see why he was acting so strange, why he looked so scared.

There was a mountain there indeed, but this mountain was not made from grass, trees or any other form of nature: this mountain was made of dead bodies.

Chapter 15

Cup Final

The chants of 'MON BUCCANEERS!' filled the air as hundreds of thousands of people wearing red and brown, looking like autumn leaves, shuffled towards the stadium in anticipation of the Cup Final. The entire population of Lowerton had been given a day off – unpaid, of course – to attend the match and in the centre of the mass was Jamie, heart pounding with excitement, the first game she was attending in over two years. She had not even kicked a ball out of frustration.

'North Stand… ne'er been there,' she said. 'We used ta sit in the South Stand.' After saying this a sense of dread came over her as she wished for her Granda to be with her.

'Ack, it's alright, but we're way up in the clouds, ye can hardly see a thing,' Billy replied.

Putting her hand in her pocket she searched for her ticket but it was not there, it was not in her usual pocket. Where could it be? She patted all of her other pockets, frantically putting her hands to the bottom of each one, but there was nothing. She went pale, stopped on the spot and put her hand to her forehead. Billy walked in front of her not noticing a thing, still chatting about the North Stand.

Herds of people trotted past Jamie as she was stuck to the spot, not knowing what to do. She put her hand back into her original pocket, the one she knew that she had put her ticket in and, hey presto, there it was. She frowned at her own stupidity. But this was her usual pre-match routine, always checking that she had her ticket, thinking she had lost it only to find it in the usual spot. Clutching it in her hand as if it was the last ticket in the world, she dodged her way through the crowd to catch up with Billy, who was still chatting nonsense.

'You fancy a burger?' he asked.

'Definitely, and some chips, full a' ketchup.'

The smell of deep fat frying hit their nostrils as they waited patiently in line for their food, a line that was at least twenty deep.

'Surely he'll nat start. He's bin 'arrific this season,' Jamie heard a man in front say, she could only see the back of his red leather jacket.

'Aye, bu' is young,' came the unmistakably wobbly voice of a drunk man, whose face was white as a ghost, eyes pointing in all directions. 'Giv'a boy'a break man!'

'Nah mate, ya need ta prove yerself and he 'asn't done it! Ya see a' state a 'im last week?' said a squeaky voice up ahead. Jamie frowned at Billy, who shrugged his shoulders as if to say 'told you so!'

'MON BUCCANEERS!' she yelled. All of a sudden the arguing men in front started an old chant and it echoed across the outside of the stadium until Jamie and Billy had reached the front of the queue and ordered their food.

No worries. No cares. Just burgers, football and a bit of a chant.

Chomping down, the ketchup spilled all over her chin. After mopping it up and licking her fingers clean, she took another bite. Paradise.

To get to the North Stand, Jamie and Billy had to make their way around to the other side of the stadium, and as they got halfway around Jamie noticed a parting in the crowd and her heart exploded.

'The team's here, let's go!' All thoughts of food hit the back of her mind as she battled through the masses, trying to force her way to the front. But again, she was met by brown and red leather and the back pockets of jeans. She stood on her tiptoes trying to see inside the bus but the curtains were drawn.

Hmm… strange, she thought, usually the team would wave out of window at the fans and having seen her puzzled face, Billy gave her a knowing look.

The bus came to a stop and between the gaps of the people in front Jamie was able to catch a glimpse of each player descending the steps, hoods up and whizzing into the stadium without a wave or even a look. The fans gave each player a cheer until the last one came out and angry tension took over, bottles, coins and burgers were thrown from all directions as he scurried into the ground.

'SHITE!'

'NOT FIT TO WEAR THE SHIRT!'

'DISGRACE!'

'GET OUT OF OUR CLUB!'

Dave pulled his hood down, glad to get through the ruckus having been hit on a regular basis, usually finding himself wiping away the smell of urine. Today was different, he waited for a few seconds until the doors closed behind Jimmy and then made his exit. Like a little rat he got through the doors without being hit by a thing.

Pre-match routine of abuse!

Walking through the Hall of Fame he tried to blank out everything around him, headphones on, music blasting Rodrigo Y Gabriela – 'Triveni', psyching himself up for what lay ahead. A Cup Final with the Buccaneers! Can it get any better?

The online forums had been going crazy all week about whether or not he should play, and he was glad that Coach Alan had told them the line-up the day before. Knowing that he was starting filled Dave with confidence, although it was hard to shake the resounding results of the polls, with 85% of supporters voting that he should not play in the Final and a further 90% not wanting him to be in the team next season. Although he was told by everyone and their mother to ignore the internet, it was impossible!

Having reached the door of the changing room, he pushed down on the handle and as soon as the door was ajar, the smell of Lynx and hairspray hit him. Taking his bag off his back and setting it on the bench beside his shirt, he took a seat and listened to the last notes of 'Triveni' before removing his earphones and carefully placing them in the front pocket of his bag. The earphones pocket, nothing else was to go in there.

A glance around at everyone else showed that they were in the middle of their own pre-match routine, most of them doing their hair, others had headphones on, eyes closed and bopping to the beat. Legs were bouncing up and down in nervous anticipation and the only sound was the thumping of two of the lads playing head tennis.

Taking a deep breath he stripped to his underwear before going through his usual routine. Shorts, shirt, left sock, right sock, left boot, right boot and finally slip the shin pads in. He rested his hands on his knees and waited for Coach Alan.

'Right lads, you know the team, I went through it yesterday,' he said after storming through the door, not waiting for anyone or anything. 'Just go out there and win! There's no two ways about it!' The usual silence met Coach Alan before he put his two thumbs up, thumbs which looked more like pig's hooves, and left the changing room.

A few moments later, when the team were ready, they made their way onto the field with Dave at the front, wanting to be the first player out before the warm-up so he could see the crowd. He also knew that being the first player out would take the crowd by surprise and they would not have enough time to get their missiles ready for him.

Although the atmosphere was nowhere near as good as when he was in the stands, he could still not get over the fact that he was being cheered and jeered by thousands of people.

As with every game of the season, the first place he jogged to was the South Stand, looking for any sign of Jamie.

Where could he be? This is the Cup Final! Dropping his head he rolled a ball from one foot to the other, effortlessly lifting it in the air before performing a number of different keepy-ups.

'Oi, Dave, you're shite!' one man yelled from the crowd, which initiated a chorus of laughter. Dave continued his keepy-ups, trying to drown out the crowd just like Fergus used to say…

Some of the other lads had started rondos or paired off, playing long passes to each other. Dave tried to get involved with them at the start of the season, but his teammates did not want him to play, worried that they would be associated with the weak link.

So he continued to do tricks on his own, alone with his thoughts, just the way he liked it since he had last seen Jamie and since Fergus had passed away. Flicking the ball high into the air, the names of the team started to be called across the loudspeaker, big cheers after each one, until the name DAVE BLANCH was followed by a low murmur.

'How's that wee rat gat on!?' a burly bald-headed man shouted from in front of Jamie, pointing his finger at the field with each word he spoke. When he got no answer he flung his arms up in disgust, shooing the field from his sight before slumping on his seat and muttering, 'Ah, I dunno anymore,' and continuing some form of rant to no one in particular.

'What's wiv all 'is negative stuff?' Jamie said, throwing her hand towards the man.

'Told ya, is nat the same. All these players from Middleton comin' over, we jus' don't cannect wiv 'em anymore.'

'Still gotta support the team, though!'

'Dat's the fing... a lat o' the fans aren't actually fans. They jus' come fer the atmosfere.'

'What atmosphere?' Jamie replied, holding her arms out to the sides like a messiah, glaring around the stadium at the supporters who were finishing their burgers, laughing and chatting. Chatting not chanting. 'Where's a' songs?'

Billy shrugged his shoulders, raised his eyebrows and shook his head in that 'told you so' manner.

'Remember we used ta sit in the South,' he said, pointing to the opposite side. 'Well nai, cos it was seen as such a great atmosfere, it's bin filled wif tourists who wanna have an experience. Only… 'cos it's fulla 'em, there's nat much noise anymore.'

Jamie crossed her arms and stared at the field, in total silence, feeling that the only love she had left in the world, The Buccaneers, had been taken from her as well.

'Come on Jamie,' Billy said, patting her shoulder, trying unsuccessfully to cheer her up. 'Sure we've no time fer these matches anymore wif work.'

She shrugged his hand off and continued glaring. From up here she could only see the blur of dots on the field, like a line of ants walking towards the tunnel and back into the changing rooms for their final match preparations.

Moments later the crowd were on their feet, blasting out 'The Good Old Buccaneers' as the players returned to the pitch. Jamie stood on her seat, hand to her chest, screaming every word at the top of her lungs, purely lost in the moment.

When the game got underway The Buccaneers had a lot of the ball, playing it from side to side, defence, midfield, defence, goalkeeper, defence, midfield, sideways, back, constant possession, possession, possession, no risks, no thrills, no atmosphere.

Jamie noticed that when it did go up to the little player behind the striker, he looked forward first before turning and playing it back. There was something familiar about his movements but she could not quite put her finger on it.

Possession. Keep possession.

She leaned over to Billy and whispered in his ear, 'This is boring.'

In total contrast to the days when she could not hear what Wee Dave was yelling at her, Billy heard every word as clear as day. Again, he shrugged and said, 'Dunno how many times I 'ave ta tell ya, it's diff'rent!'

Twenty minutes had passed, no shots, no corners, no NOISE, in fact no anything except The Buccaneers' 100% possession.

'Ere, if all the Middleton bais are over there,' she said, leaning in to Billy's ear and pointing to the South Stand, 'then surely this is all our lat over 'ere.' She stood up, wheeled around and saw that the North Stand was packed to the rafters.

She cupped her hand to her mouth. 'MON BUCCANEERS!!'

There was a murmur around the stand, as if everyone had been thinking the same but were too afraid to do anything. One person about forty rows below got to his feet, wheeled around to look at her and shouted, 'MON BUCCANEERS!!'

A few more people in different parts of the stand... 'MON BUCCANEERS!!'

Within minutes, the whole of the North Stand was in harmony, singing at the top of their voices, bouncing up and down, bringing back the good old days, bringing back the NOISE.

The world seemed to stop as the North Stand erupted, the players on the pitch had never experienced an atmosphere like this... with the exception of one. The NOISE was incredible, deafening, electrifying and it brought Dave back to better times, the good old days when he and Jamie would cheer and chant and jump and bounce in the stands.

A smile formed on his face as he started to chant along, remembering the days of...

'Hang on, they're cheering me now! I'm playing!' Shaking himself awake he stared at the rest of the players, who were frozen to the spot, gawping at the crowd and not knowing what to do.

'Oi, gimme the ball!' Dave shouted to Gary, who had it in his hands, waiting to take a throw in. He, like all the rest on field, was looking to the North Stand to see what the commotion was.

'GARY!' Dave yelled but still no reaction. Sprinting forwards, Dave threw his arms out, shoving Gary in the shoulder. Gary turned his face towards him, mouth agape with his tongue resting on his bottom lip, still in a daze. Dave pushed him again and after no reaction, he drew his right hand behind his left shoulder and let rip with a backhand to Gary's face. Red knuckle marks appeared on his cheek when Gary finally came to his senses.

'THE BALL, GIMME THE BALL!' Dave screamed, this time pointing his two hands at the ball then vigorously at his feet. Eventually, Gary put his hands behind his neck and threw the ball to Dave. Scanning the field showed him that every player was stuck to the spot, like fuss-ball players, and it was the first time in his life that he thought that the training of dribbling around static cones and shooting into an empty net was worthwhile.

1–0.

The rest of the team only came to life because the South Stand had joined the North in creating an emporium of NOISE, like surround sound at full blast with Wee Dave in the middle, living for the moment, stuck in the present.

When do we really live in the present? When do YOU really live in the present?

The game kicked off after the goal and Wee Dave quickly won possession, playing it back to the safety of the defence. Looking around the field again, he knew he had this game in the palm of his hand.

'Remember to drown out the noise, relaaaaax and focus on your game,' came the words from Fergus. *Oh Fergus, how I miss you!* A tear was forming until he remembered where he was, what the advice was supposed to mean.

'Right, let's go, FOCUS.'

Did I say that out loud?

Who cares!

He snapped back into action the moment the ball was played to his feet, laying it back with his first touch to someone in brown and red, he had no idea who, he only saw the kit. He was so focussed on his next move which was to swivel away from his marker and gallop beyond the striker. As he was doing this, the centre midfielder passed the ball first time to the striker, who saw Wee Dave's run and flicked it through with the outside of his foot.

One-on-one with the goalkeeper. Like all those times playing one-on-one with Slyme, one-on-one with Jamie.

Oh where is Jamie. He should be playing instead of me.

Wee Dave duly slotted the ball to the side of the keeper's outstretched arm, catching the inside of the post before it rolled into the net. Arms outstretched and wheeling to the side like an airplane, he caught a glimpse of Coach Alan sprinting... well, waddling down the touchline like a big fat penguin. If Wee Dave had never been in the stands before he could have been forgiven for thinking that Coach Alan had caused an earthquake, but he knew where the NOISE was coming from, he knew why the ground was shaking.

2–0.

Jamie should be playing WITH me, not instead of me, he thought as the game kicked off again.

Half-time came and went in the blink of an eye. Coach Alan said some words, did some finger pointing, but Wee Dave had absolutely no interest, only wanting to get out there and play the game he loved.

The second half got underway. Possession. Possession. Possesszzzzzzz.

Fuck Possession. Boring football. Let's see some goals! Let's take some risks!

Wee Dave dropped deeper and deeper trying to get the ball. He nicked in front of one his own midfielders, stealing the ball from his feet and with a drop of the shoulder he was past one, past another, no need for fancy tricks, just stick to a change of direction and a change of speed. The best way to beat a defender.

A little look up to the field, little look at the ball, little look to the field, little look to the ball.

The little looks made it clear that the left winger was in space so he drilled one into his feet. As the ball was en route the opposition full-back stepped up, putting instant pressure on the player receiving the ball but leaving space behind for Wee Dave to accelerate into. A perfectly timed pass from the left winger and he'd be one-on-one with the last defender, an oaf who could barely move. He'd get past him easily…

But the ball did not come. Instead, the ball was played back to the defenders, safety first. Possession. AAAAARRGHHHH!!!

Wee Dave was enraged and like a man possessed he sprinted to the left winger, grabbed him by the scruff of the neck and told him in no uncertain terms to play it forward the next time.

'But Coach Alan—' was the brittle response, before Wee Dave cut him off.

'I don't care about Coach Alan, we're here to score goals. Just make sure you play me through the next time!'

The last thirty minutes of the Final were flawless from The Buccaneers, their best performance of the season by a country mile. Wee Dave covered every blade of grass, producing wizardry and artistry on the pitch which no team could live with, inspiring the rest of the team to play exciting and attacking football.

Final score. 7–0. Wee Dave scored five, he had no idea who scored the others.

An almighty BANG made the hair on Jamie's arms rise. Another bang and her heart was dancing. Another bang and she looked at Billy, who was grinning from ear to ear. Crouching down, he wrapped his arms around her waist and Jamie was whooshed into the air, trying to look to the field but finding it impossible as Billy's bouncing forced her to hold on for dear life.

'Billy, Billy, BILLY!' she laughed. 'Hold me steady.' Clutching at his head, her cheeks were in so much pain with the laughter, her heart racing at a million beats per second and tears were forming with the pure emotion of everything.

'We've just won a CUP FINAL!!!' she screamed. 'The CUP. AAAAGGGGHHH!!!'

When Billy had steadied himself she tried to look at the field through the red and brown haze from the flares, but it was a blur. She could see the hordes of supporters in the South Stand bouncing up and down, alternating their arms in the air as they jumped in unison, like a dance, a work of art and as one famous chant faded, another began. The drums were next, Jamie raising her arms high above her head and clapping along with the beat, slowly at first but picking up speed with each clap.

CLAP… CLAP… CLAP… CLAP… CLAP… CLAP… CLAP. CLAPCLAPCLAPCLAP.

After the drumming and clapping could go no quicker, Jamie saw the man from the front of the stand with the microphone starting the next chant. The same man that had always been there, tattoos still evident on his skinhead, a ring in his nose, but looking at least thirty years older than when she had last seen him. But he still pumped his fist in the air with the same passion and intensity that made the rest of the crowd join in.

'I can't see a thing from up here,' Jamie shouted from Billy's shoulders but he couldn't hear a word. She tapped him on the head, and pointing to the ground she mouthed 'Let me down', to which he stooped his back and she stepped onto her seat. Cupping her hand to his ear she yelled, 'I'm gonna try and get closer,' and when he smiled at her she knew he did not have a clue what she said, so again she mouthed, 'I'm going down there,' pointing to the field.

Billy held his thumb and index finger in a circle, the universal sign of 'Okay'.

Squirming through the crowd was easy for Jamie, she was still so small and in a matter of minutes she found herself at the very front of the upper tier, leaning against the metal bars. Looking to the lower stand she could see the flags waving and the fans partying. It must have been thirty minutes since the final whistle had blown, but not one person in the stadium had left. From

Jamie's position she was able to see the dots coming together and throwing one player into the air, the one player who was booed at the start, the new signing who had gone from zero to hero.

At the front railings she still needed to squint to see the field, just making out the team who were doing a celebratory lap with the Cup firmly in the hands of the hero. She stared at the Cup as the team walked slowly around the opposite side of the field, the hero pondering a little longer at the North Stand while the rest of the team moved behind the goal, making their way closer to the South Stand, closer to Jamie.

But her eyes were still fixed on the Cup.

By now, her stomach was being pushed into the railing in front of her and she tried to push against the tide, but she could not unjam her hands, she did not have the strength, so she kept her eyes forward as the team moved around the field. Still squinting, the team had passed but the Cup was coming into her view and as Jamie moved her eyes from the Cup to the hero, the hero to the Cup and then back to the hero, her heart skipped with excitement as she realised that Dave Blanch, the hero of the Cup Final, was better known to her as Wee Dave.

'Oh my Smite, he's done it, HE'S DONE IT,' she screamed. She brought her hands to her cheeks to wipe away the tears of joy, but she could not stop them, smiling like a fool, eyes still fixed on Wee Dave.

'Wee Dave, Wee Dave,' she shouted, frantically trying to get his attention. She tried to wave her arms but they were stuck, the thousands behind beginning to crush forward to get a better look at the trophy.

This was the most amazing experience of Jamie's life, more than she ever could have wished for, Paradise. She could not wait to see Wee Dave again, she could not wait to hear the story of him playing for their beloved team, she had many stories to tell him from her days of construction. The thought of her and Wee Dave being reunited filled her head as the railing in front of her collapsed and she was in the first row of thousands of raining bodies to land in the stand below.

And as she hurtled through the air she caught one last glimpse of the love of her life, and her final memory was a happy one.

Chapter 16

The Game He Loved

Three years later...

He pulled the sunglasses from the visor and put his foot to the floor, the sounds of the latest heavy metal song blasting from the speakers as he raced through the winding streets. Trees and mansions lined both sides of the road, some of the neighbours mowing their lawns, others playing football with their kids, others swimming.

He took a deep breath and the smell of barbecue hit his nose, the red glow from the setting sun gave the place a relaxing feel, crystal blue skies making it all the more wonderful, not a cloud in sight.

As he arrived home, he slowed his shiny red Ferrari and reached for the button under the steering wheel, opening the cast-iron gate to reveal a track leading up to the family castle. He left the car in its usual place in the garage, between his yellow Porsche and his mum's silver Aston Martin. A push of another button on the dashboard and the door slid upwards, allowing him to exit the vehicle and walk past the other ten or so cars that were there.

He had lost count by now.

Walking out of the garage and across the lawn, he stroked his hand across the helicopter as he resumed the 100-metre walk up the steps and to the balcony. On the way up he took his phone out and ordered himself a beer and chicken pasta, and as soon as he reached the top his clothes were off and he dived into the pool, a few lengths to cool down after another tough game for City.

While he was drying himself the butler came with his order. He scoffed his pasta and lifted the ice-cold bottle, taking a swig before settling into the bubbling hot water of his jacuzzi. The first gulp was always the most relaxing, that ice-cold liquid running through the back of his throat and into his chest.

He put the bottle down and, leaning over the side of the jacuzzi, he scanned the City. The sun had completely set and he looked longingly across to Lowerton, where that fateful night had made him the successful player he was today, but would always play on his heart as he remembered the thousands of statistics, as he thought of his best friend Jamie and the times they had spent together...

Where could he be?

It had been over four years, but David still considered Jamie the best thing that had ever happened to him.

This ritual was always the same for David, after playing for City he would reminisce about the good old days when he played in Lowerton, when he loved the game of football. It was no longer a game for him, it was not fun, it was a job. Although he had done everything the City had asked of him, all that Society had asked of him, excelling in School, exceeding expectations in football by becoming the youngest ever player in the League of the Sky, lock, stock and barrel... All he wanted to do was play with Jamie. Even play with Slyme. Play.

A swig and a sigh.

The sky was pitch black by now and on came the dancing lights of Upperton as people started to party, music blaring from speakers in all directions.

Another swig, another sigh.

From his vantage point he glanced across Upperton and into Middleton, where the main two streets shone like two runways, making a giant cross in the centre with the smaller lights from the houses showing that there was life there. David thought of the families cooking dinner, watching TV, studying, just like he had done in the past.

Another swig, another sigh.

Finally he looked down to Lowerton, darkness, darkness, darkness... This darkness across Lowerton made the monument of Mr Smite glow even brighter, a beacon of light pointing his finger across the whole City.

'I'm watching you,' it seemed to say.

A final gulp of his drink and David dried himself, put his fluffy red robe on and made his way into the castle.

'Great game today, son,' Dad said after he had walked in. 'Do you want to watch the highlights?'

'Nah Dad, I'm okay. I'm just gonna lie down for a bit, maybe read that new book from Mr Stout.'

'Okay, see you in the morning.'

'Night,' he replied, dragging himself up the stairs.

'Everything okay, son?' Mum asked, when he got to the top.

'Yeah, just tired,' he mumbled. 'I'm gonna have an early night.'

'Okie doke,' she said brightly. 'See you in the morning.'

'Night,' he replied.

Collapsing on his bed he stared at the ceiling, clasping his hands behind his head before closing his eyes. He had everything now, everything he deserved, everything he had ever worked for. He was told this would lead to happiness.

 But he always thought of football as fun. Where had the game gone? What happened to the game he loved?

He turned on to his side and fell asleep. He should have been dreaming of the bright future that lay ahead of him, he was still a young man of eighteen years old. Instead, he dreamed of glory days gone by.

BV - #0068 - 101218 - C0 - 234/156/12 - PB - 9781780915821